Contents

To find an establishment, look for it's entry number on each pa

vouchers

All the usuals plus our **Special FOODIE Vouchers** for this year, find them at the back

award

Nominate your favourite restaurant for an award and you could win a meal for two

---

Key to symbols

Families welcome	Extensive wines by the glass (10 or more)	Smoking area provided	FOODIE reader recommended
Wheel chair access	Real ale	Chef profile	**£5** £5 off VOUCHER
Garden/patio area	Live music or entertainment	**FT** Fair Trade produce used where possible	10% 10% off VOUCHER
Accommodation available	Conference room	**O** Organic produce used where possible	Free bottle of **wine** VOUCHER
Extensive Wine List (30 or more)	Dog friendly	**DC** Dining Card	**V** Special FOODIE VOUCHER

Average cost of 3 course meal without drinks

A £20 or below	**D** £30 - £35
B £20 - £25	**E** £35 - £40
C £25 - £30	**F** £40 or above

THE FOODIE voucher symbols: Please check individual entries for which FOODIE vouchers are accepted and any establishment terms (terms and conditions apply)

Introduction

Before you engross yourself in this very special edition of THE FOODIE GUIDE, let me first of all thank everyone who has purchased the guide over the past 10 years. This support for a local publication, which is produced because of its reader's local knowledge of the very best in fine food and wine, makes THE FOODIE GUIDE quite unique. In this tenth edition, once again we share our passion for discovering good service, excellent food and a superb commitment to quality.

The broad uniformity and blandness of the supermarket and internet shop has given rise to a wave of diversity and contrast when it comes to the Farm Shop experience. Which, I think you will agree, is an event to be savoured and not a weekly chore to be rushed. This creates great optimism for the future and we have included many in this edition for you to try.

We look forward to creating Edition 11 of THE FOODIE GUIDE as always with your help and with the aim of keeping you informed of the very best in our local area for food and wine. And remember, we always welcome your thoughts.

Paul Allen
Editor

photograph courtesy of The Bricklayers Arms

Foreword

by our guest chef for this year
Phil Fanning

In a year in which we have revelled being British, celebrating the Queen's Jubilee and hosting the Olympics, I am more proud than ever to be a chef. Working in the hospitality industry has highlighted another of our country's strengths – great British produce.

We are extremely fortunate that Bedfordshire and the surrounding counties offer a fantastic variety of amazing local produce. From farmers markets, to butchers, to delis, to brilliant foodie businesses like the Ampthill Cookshop, I am constantly surprised by choice and quality. It is this quality that has formed the foundation of the thriving culinary scene in the region for locals and visitors to enjoy. I haven't lived in the area for long but I have stumbled across some really impressive suppliers and producers since I've been here. The most interesting for me have been: The Woburn Estate and their Venison which is sensational; Aylesbury Escargot who produce the best snails I've ever used; Martin Risboro who consistently supplies the finest of fish; and Redbourne School in Ampthill, whose school farm will be supplying us with our rare bred suckling pigs this year, lovingly reared to our exact specifications by Ben and the students.

Since becoming Head Chef at Paris House, Woburn in 2010, I've had an amazing journey, the highlight being awarded a Michelin-star in February 2011. We celebrated this achievement with members of the community and local suppliers. "A workman is only as good as his tools," and this award also pays homage to their creativity and excellence.

I do hope you enjoy reading The Foodie Guide, which will give an insight into the culinary gems of the area. I certainly hope discovering the gastronomic brilliance in this region gives you as much pleasure as it has done for me.

Phil Fanning
Head Chef
Paris House, Woburn

Food for thought

It all began......

Watching my Dad cook Sunday lunch, a labour of love for him, an absolute joy for me and my family. He had a habit of being able to turn any meal into something special...empty plates were a regular event in our home.

At School, Domestic Science was only available to the girls, shock that a boy of my age would want to go into a kitchen and learn how to cook. With some persuasion I was allowed to join the class for my final year at School. And so began my life in catering.

It was an interesting career choice, with five other students choosing catering, sadly I am the only one left still cooking. I worked in a variety of establishments after my training – mostly English based restaurants, but always with the dream of having my own place. I had to put my dreams on hold for a few years, as I had four hungry mouths to feed. When the youngest child was 14 in 1997, I was able to fulfil my dream, I along with Janet, whom I married in 1997, took over The Royal Oak, East Lavant near Chichester. I was able to put all my years of working for other people, and watching their success, into practice. We then, in 2001, moved into Chichester and opened a restaurant. During this time, I have seen foods come and go in popularity, lots of new foods available

and the Public have also become much more interested in food.

My move to The Betsey Wynne was by chance in July 2007, and for two years I worked as Head Chef. Since becoming Landlord I am able to get more involved in the future of the pub, and my aim is to achieve growth of the business, using our own and surrounding farms and their facilities. We are extending the restaurant, to be able to offer Conferencing and Private Parties etc. Also, we are hoping to build a Wedding Barn, and open a Farm Shop, next to the pub, within the next few years. And to keep building the Village Cooperative with the allotments to help provide some of the home grown produce.

I along with Janet am now tasked with turning The Betsey Wynne into a multi-faceted business, we welcome all input and always recognise the importance of our customers and their views. As a six year old business we are still an infant in the business world and have a long way to go. But with modern eating habits shaping our outlook, it is and will be an interesting journey.

Kevin Close
Landlord/Head Chef
The Betsey Wynne

Main Street
Adstock
Buckinghamshire
MK18 2JN
Tel: 01296 712584
Fax: 01296 715375
Email: enquiries@theoldthatchedinn.co.uk
www.theoldthatchedinn.co.uk

The Old Thatched Inn

Gastro Pub, Adstock

THE FOODIE GUIDE
Diner Review

"Excellent service, wonderful food and a great atmosphere."

Aylesbury Vale's Village Pub of the Year 2010, The Old Thatched Inn is a countryside gastro-pub which offers its customers a unique blend of high quality dining hosted in a relaxed and comfortable environment. Situated in the picturesque village of Adstock, Buckinghamshire, The Old Thatched Inn dates back to 1702 and combines this heritage with a menu that fuses the freshest seasonal ingredients cooked with emphasis on taste, with modern presentation.

Managed by owner and ex-chef Andrew Judge and his wife Lisa, the team at the locally-celebrated Old Thatched Inn believes in casual dining and sources the finest, freshest ingredients from a multitude of small specialist food producers and suppliers, preferring local and organic produce whenever possible.

Favourites on the seasonally-changing menu include locally sourced rare-breed lamb, an extensive fish selection delivered direct from Billingsgate market, and home-made ice creams, with further specials that change daily which excite the mind and the palate. The Old Thatched Inn also boasts a wine list featuring close to 40 selections and is one of the only gastro-pubs in the county to have five fine ales on tap along with a vast shelf selection of malt whiskies and other spirits from across the globe.

With five qualified chefs and eight full and part-time waiting staff, the service at The Old Thatched Inn is professional, attentive and discrete. A welcoming and comfortable waiting lounge, a generous bar area seating 35 and large conservatory seating 60 people, make The Old Thatched Inn the ideal venue for both casual dining, business lunches and special events.

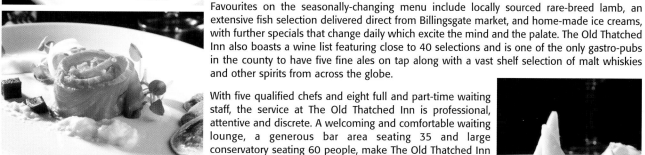

Opening times: 12 noon - 11.00 pm
Food served: **Mon-Fri** 12 noon - 2.30 pm & 6.00 - 9.30 pm
Sat 12 noon - 9.30 pm **Sun** 12 noon - 8.00 pm
Restaurant times may vary due to season

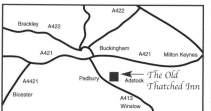

Brackley A422
A422
A421 Buckingham A421 Milton Keynes
A4421 Padbury Adstock *The Old Thatched Inn*
Bicester A413 Winslow

£5 10%
Vouchers valid Mon-Thurs

The Carriage House Restaurant

Claydon House
Middle Claydon
Buckinghamshire
MK18 2EX
Tel: 01296 730004
Email: eat@thecarriagehouserestaurant.co.uk
www.thecarriagehouserestaurant.co.uk

Within the courtyard of the magnificent Claydon Estate, you'll find The Carriage House Restaurant, offering you renowned cuisine surrounded by beautiful gardens and breathtaking parkland.

Following 18 exciting years running Oxfordshire's famous restaurant boat, "Rosamund The Fair", the owners, Tim Matthews and Sophia Goodford, have transformed The Carriage House Restaurant into an opulent dining experience that's hard to resist.

Head Chef/Proprietor Tim Matthews and his team use only the very best, carefully sourced produce, offering you beautiful modern British cuisine. The finest meats from the local butcher in Padbury, fresh game from the Claydon Estate and seasonal fruit and vegetables from the walled kitchen garden at Claydon are used to create delicious and imaginative dishes for you to savour.

The menus change regularly with the restaurant open for lunches every day except Thursdays and Fridays, open for dinner every Saturday evening, dinner for 10 or more any evening and for a Special Event every month. Why not look at our Special Events listed on our website including annual mushroom forays in the Claydon woods with John Wright, mushroom expert from The River Cottage.

On Sundays you'll find indulgent two and three course lunches.

An ideal venue for weddings, parties and corporate events throughout the year, you can enjoy exclusive use of the restaurant any day of the week. A quiet, professional approach ensures your event is truly memorable. We look forward to welcoming you.

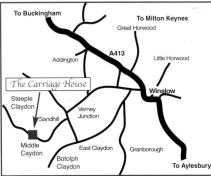

THE FOODIE GUIDE
Diner Review

"A lovely restaurant for a special occasion, excellent service and attention to detail, the food is sublime!"

Food service times:
Mon-Wed 12.00 pm - 3.00 pm
Thur-Fri Closed **Sat-Sun** 12.00 pm - 3.00 pm
Saturday evenings from 6.00 pm and Special Event timing from our website (bookings required).
Private parties and weddings at any time throughout the year.

Lunch Dinner

£5

the swan inn

Broughton Road
Milton Keynes Village
Milton Keynes
Buckinghamshire MK10 9AH
Tel: 01908 665240
Fax: 01908 395081
Email: info@theswan-mkvillage.co.uk
www.theswan-mkvillage.co.uk

This 13th Century thatched pub features flagstone floors, an open fire set in an inglenook fireplace and a sheltered orchard garden. Sympathetically renovated, the interior is an eclectic mix of traditional charm and contemporary chic with warm fabrics and clever use of natural finishes. The dining room overlooks a terrace set in the garden and is ideal for summer dining.

Real ales feature alongside an extensive wine list boasting over 20 wines by the glass and the range of soft drinks include a selection of organic fruit juices and lemonades. An open plan kitchen prepares a simple yet creative menu, changed monthly in line with the seasons, based on excellent value and local ingredients, including herbs from its own garden.

Sunday lunch is a traditional affair with a selection of succulent roasts and plentiful veg and potatoes. Daily changing specials plus a selection of lighter lunch items complete the food offer.

Service is brisk and friendly by the knowledgeable staff who herald from around the globe. The atmosphere is always lively given the core group of locals who support this warm and welcoming pub in the heart of the original Milton Keynes Village. A real find.

THE FOODIE GUIDE
Diner Review

"A very popular place, the food and service can't be faulted."

Food service times:
Mon-Thur 12.00 pm - 3.00 pm &
6.00 pm - 9.30 pm
Fri-Sat 12.00 pm - 3.00 pm &
6.00 pm - 10.00 pm
Sun 12.00 pm - 6.00 pm

£5 10%

bell&bear
villagepub&restaurant

12 High Street, Emberton, Buckinghamshire MK46 5DH
Tel: 01234 711565
Email: hello@bellandbear.net
www.bellandbear.net

THE FOODIE GUIDE
Diner Review

"The choice here is exceptional, the quality top notch and in a typically English pub setting."

The Bell & Bear is a community focused traditional village pub with an intimate separate restaurant serving interesting hyper local modern British cuisine. Jon and Sophie met whilst working on the Isle of Wight and bought the pretty grade II listed freehouse in 2010 whilst aged just 26. They have since forged a name for themselves in the local area, and beyond, for serving interesting local produce from field to plate with evenings and Sunday lunches booking up weeks even months in advance.

The pub has received accolades from national press and guide books and is unique in providing two very separate experiences. A village pub serving CAMRA award winning local real ales, interesting craft beers and imported German Pilsner, Helles and Weizen beer on draught. The bar is the hub of the local community. The pub has championed local cider and was part of the success of 2011 Champion Cider of Britain "Virtual Orchard" from Milton Keynes. Dogs are welcomed in the bar area where sandwiches are also available at lunch.

In the restaurant, all of more than 50 wines are available by the glass including a selection of "natural" wines, organic and bio-dynamic from boutique producers and lesser known terroirs. Recommendations for every dish are incorporated into the every changing list. The menu boards change daily and showcase local produce. The pub has become renowned for it's 60 day dry aged pedigree "Hereford" beef from Monica Brown and it's slow reared guinea fowls from Pastures Farm. A sample three course meal could include hand dived scallops, pea puree and seaweed caviar, cannon and rissole of local lamb with sweet potato and courgette fritter and chocolate torte, sea salt butterscotch and milk ice cream.

The Bell & Bear

Olney Rd

To Olney

Newport Road

A509

High St

Newton Rd

To Miton Keynes

Food service times:
Tue 6.30 pm - 9.00 pm
Wed - Sat 12.30 pm - 2.00 pm & 6.30 pm - 9.00 pm
Sun 12.30 pm - 2.00 pm

  £5 10%

      FT O

THE BULL INN

9 Market Place
Olney
Buckinghamshire MK46 4EA
Tel: 01234 711470
Fax: 01234 241862
Email: thebullolney@gmail.com
www.thebullolney.com

OLNEY

Situated in the heart of Olney's market place is the 400 year old Bull Inn, formerly a coaching inn for the landed gentry. The Bulls character, warmth, friendly and professional service makes it a perfect venue for any occasion.

The Bull has a well earned reputation for well kept cask ales and is renowned for Sunday lunches in addition to a freshly prepared, varied menu which attracts visitors from all over the local area. Extensive gardens and walled courtyards make the Bull an ideal place to unwind and relax.

James Lomax and Mark Girling (pictured left), both chefs with over 30 years experience between them, aim to provide simple well cooked food, made from the best ingredients and sourced locally whenever possible.

The menu changes regularly to reflect the changing seasons and availability of fresh local produce.

THE FOODIE GUIDE
Diner Review

"An excellent place to go for lunch, we combined this with a lovely stroll around the interesting shops in Olney."

Food service times:
Mon-Fri 12.00 pm - 2.30 pm & 6.00 pm - 9.30 pm
Sat 12.00 pm - 4.00 pm & 6.00 pm - 9.30 pm
Sun 12.00 pm - 4.00 pm

10% DC

     FT O Ⓐ

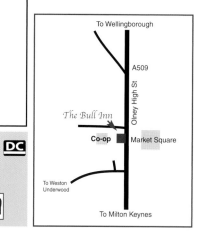

To Wellingborough

A509

Olney High St

The Bull Inn

Co-op   Market Square

To Weston Underwood

To Milton Keynes

THE BETSEY WYNNE

21 Mursley Road
Swanbourne
Buckinghamshire
MK17 0SH
Tel: 01296 720825
Email: info@thebetseywynne.co.uk
www.thebetseywynne.co.uk

THE FOODIE GUIDE
Diner Review

*"Really gorgeous gardens
and well worth a visit as
the food is freshly cooked
and very tasty."*

The Betsey Wynne

FREE HOUSE

The Betsey Wynne is part of the Swanbourne Estate in the small village of Swanbourne in North Buckinghamshire which has been owned by the Fremantle family for over 200 years. The opening of The Betsey Wynne, named after one of the Estate's colourful ancestors, is the result of many years of careful planning by the Estate and a quiet determination by the present owner to preserve and promote country life.

Built by the Swanbourne Estate in true local style, this free house has a large bar, comfortable leather sofas, open log fires and an impressive oak beamed dining hall. The snug, with its large inglenook fireplace and flagstone floor is suitable for meetings or private dining. In the summer, guests can enjoy the large garden with an old red tractor and play house for children.

Kevin Close is the Chef/Landlord, a popular Northern chef with an eye for detail, who favours classic English cuisine. A former landlord and restaurant owner with years of experience, including chef at the "Mild May" at the Glyndebourne Opera, now part of The Betsey Wynne folklore.

The Betsey Wynne aims to be a true "local" farm pub. Using their farm's own produce and supporting other local farmers as far as possible. The beef comes from the Home Farm's herd of pedigree Aberdeen Angus cows. The lamb on the menu comes from the flock of pedigree Hampshire Down sheep, which some butchers refer to as the "Aberdeen Angus equivalent of the lamb counter". They have exceptional eating quality - juicy, tender and a wonderful flavour. The pork comes from a variety of local producers. Sausages are made by Betsy Duncan Smith, who also cures her hams for the pub from her Saddleback and Large Black pigs. Both are traditional native breeds, full of flavour and reared traditionally in Swanbourne. Poultry is sourced from various local suppliers depending on produce required for menus. Seasonal game and venison is sourced where possible from nearby estates and primarily the Claydon Estate. From time to time 'specials' include pheasant, partridge, pigeon and rabbit.

The Estate has reinstated a traditional orchard to produce apples, pears, plums, mulberries, quince and figs. The Fremantle family's walled garden has also been revived and under Philip Dalton, the head gardener, now produces herbs and a variety of vegetables and soft fruit.

There is a marquee available for weddings, christenings and parties. Loyalty cards and gift vouchers are also on offer.

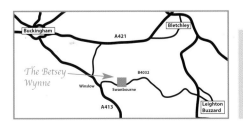

Food service times:
Mon - Fri 12.00 pm - 2.30 pm & 7.00 pm - 9.30 pm
Sat 12.00 pm - 9.30 pm
Sun 12.00 pm - 4.00 pm (8.00 pm summer) Sunday menu only

£5 10%

Vouchers accepted
Monday to Thursday only

The Crooked Billet

2 Westbrook End
Newton Longville
Buckinghamshire
MK17 0DF
Tel: 01908 373936
Fax: 01908 631979
www.thebillet.co.uk

THE FOODIE GUIDE
Diner Review

"The food here is outstanding, the presentation and service is a very high standard too."

A contemporary award winning restaurant in a traditional country pub

"THE FOODIE Award 2004, 2006, 2007, 2010, 2011 & 2012 - Bucks" - THE FOODIE GUIDE
"50 best restaurants in the UK" - The Independent Guide
"Gastro Pub Of The Year" - The Times
"Wine Pub Of The Year" - The Good Pub Guide
"Inspectors Favourite Restaurant" - Michelin Guide to Pubs
"One of the best restaurants outside of London" - Tatler Guide

Milton Keynes Restaurant of the year 2012. The Crooked Billet is a contemporary restaurant located in a traditional, thatched, British pub in the village of Newton Longville, 7 miles from Milton Keynes in Buckinghamshire.

Monthly changing A la Carte menu and daily changing lunch and dinner set menus showcase seasonal, locally sourced ingredients. While the extensive wine list offers some 200 wines by the glass.

You can enjoy simpler dishes, snacks and sandwiches in the bar area which has original oak beams and inglenook fireplaces. The real ale is credited with Cask Marque and Brewers Awards and the cheeseboard is one of the best in the country.

Please visit our website for up-to-date menus and events.

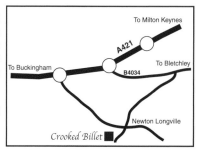

Food service times:
Lunch - **Tues-Sat** 12.00 pm - 2.00 pm **Sun** 12.30 pm - 4.00 pm
Dinner - **Mon-Thurs** 7.00 pm - 9.30 pm **Fri-Sat** 6.30 pm - 10.00 pm

Vouchers not valid Fri or Sat evening

THE PILGRIM

25 High Street
North Marston
Buckinghamshire
MK18 3PD
Tel: 01296 670969
Email: info@thepilgrimpub.co.uk
www.thepilgrimpub.co.uk

THE FOODIE GUIDE
Diner Review

"This is a very special village pub/restaurant serving delicious food, expertly prepared."

The Pilgrim Pub, formerly The Bell, was bought in December 2009 by a group of locals. They set about refurbishing the property, to make it a modern pub/restaurant that the whole village could be proud of.

Nominated for the Aylesbury Vale Pub of the Year Competition 2011, The Pilgrim has quickly established itself as a great place to eat. Whether for a quick snack from the bar menu or a relaxed evening dining from the seasonal à la carte menu. The Pilgrim is a friendly and informal restaurant and pub offering great homemade food with as many ingredients sourced locally as possible. Selected local suppliers include: Woburn Country Foods for meat and game; Derek Pigott of Aylesbury for fruit and veg; Chiltern Fish & Game for fish and game; Anthony Rowcliffe for cheese.

Head Chef Peter Godwin says, " My menu should give you a good indication of what The Pilgrim in North Marston is and what we are trying to be and achieve. The Pilgrim Restaurant is my shop window and it demonstrates my philosophy of food." Expect to find a varied selection on the menu from Roast Pork Fillet, Slow Braised Belly, Black Pudding Purée, Celeriac and Potato Dauphinoise, Jus and Creamed Savoy Cabbage with Bacon; to Devonshire Crab Thermidor, Hand Cut Triple Cooked Chips and Herb Salad. Vegetarians are also thoughtfully catered for and the dessert menu and comprehensive cheese selection is a delight.

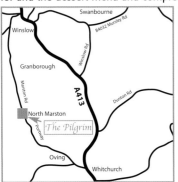

Regular events are held including a Quiz Night on Tuesdays with a 2 course quiz menu for £10 and Steak Night on a Thursday offering a selection of locally sourced 21 Day Dry Aged Steaks.

Food service times:
Mon - Thur 12.00 pm - 2.30 pm & 6.00 pm - 9.00 pm
Fri - Sat 12.00 pm - 2.30 pm & 6.00 pm - 9.30 pm
Sun 12.00 pm - 3.00 pm

£5 10%

Rajdhani

706 Midsummer Boulevard
Food Centre
Central Milton Keynes
MK9 3NT
Tel: 01908 392299
Fax: 01908 392541
www.rajdhanimk.com
Restaurant/Take-away

"As featured on BBC's Look East"

THE FOODIE GUIDE
Diner Review

"The food and welcome is consistently good here and you never know whose famous face you'll see."

As a family owned restaurant Ali and his brothers know only too well that good food, service and knowledge are all the ingredients that are required to run a good restaurant, which is why they were given "Long Standing Restaurant of the Year 2012" by MK Food & Leisure Award, all these qualities can be found here at the Rajdhani. Being a popular venue with visiting actors and actresses appearing at the nearby theatre, speaks volumes for both food and service.

The Rajdhani is regularly rated in the top 100 Indian restaurants and more recently shortlisted in the top 10 for The Best Spice Restaurant in the UK 2012. Awarded Silver for the South East region.

Ali's three highly trained chefs work hard behind the scenes ensuring that all dishes are freshly prepared using as much local produce as possible, preparing imaginative and flavoursome dishes which number a staggering 30 plus.

Both Sunday and Monday evenings the Rajdhani hold their very popular buffets and with over 25 items on offer diners are spoilt for choice.

If you've not enjoyed a take away yet then now's the time. The Rajdhani offer a free home delivery service on all orders over £12, or if you want to collect it yourself Ali is happy to give you 20% off any orders over £15 (excluding set menus and Thali dishes).

Why not take advantage of a massive 25% off your total food bill when dining in the restaurant by simply presenting their Special Foodie Voucher? (see voucher for details).

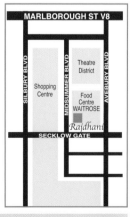

Opening times: Open 7 days a week
Mon-Thur 12.00 pm - 2.30 pm & 6.00 pm - 11.00 pm
Fri 6.00 pm - 12.00 am
Sat 12.00 pm - 2.30 pm & 6.00 pm - 12.00 am
Sun 12.00 pm - 10.30 pm

THE CARRINGTON ARMS

Cranfield Road
Moulsoe
Newport Pagnell
Buckinghamshire MK16 0HB
Tel: 01908 218050
Fax: 01908 217850
Email: enquiries@thecarringtonarms.co.uk
www.thecarringtonarms.co.uk

THE FOODIE GUIDE
Diner Review

"The freshest of food expertly prepared and absolutely delicious."

The Carrington Arms is an imposing 19th century listed building only one mile from junction 14 of the M1 in the picturesque village of Moulsoe.

For over 20 years The Carrington Arms has been famous for steaks using 21 Day Aged Bedfordshire Beef, served from a butchers counter in their open kitchen and the current owners carry on this tradition. More recently it has been selected in 'The Independent' newspaper in their top 50. The reviewer said, *"they have one of the most delicious items of food I have eaten in Britain, which is the steak marinated in Jack Daniels".*

Alongside their counter they have introduced a restaurant à la carte and a bar menu using the best in fresh local ingredients. They are immensely proud of the local produce they use, especially their meat, game and poultry with herbs and salads from their own garden. They also source local real ales from micro breweries in Cranfield, Olney and Silverstone.

The Carrington is revisiting our recent culinary past for their à la carte. Dishes with names which will be familiar to all of us such as; Prawn Cocktail, Kedgeree, Egg and Soldiers, Roast Pork and Apple Sauce, Raspberry Ripple and Death by Chocolate. But in the hands of the Carrington's Team expect their innovation and unique style to put their mark on these classics.

M1 North

Central Milton Keynes — Junction 14 — Newport Pagnell

M1 South

The Carrington Arms

There are eight recently refurbished en suite chalet style bedrooms within the gardens, each with a flat screen television, tea and coffee facilities and continental breakfast.

Food service times:
Mon-Sat 12.00 pm - 10.00 pm
Sun 12.00 pm - 9.30 pm

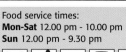 

London Road
Little Kingshill
Great Missenden
Bucks HP16 0DG
Tel: 01494 862200
Fax: 01494 862945
Email: goodfood@nagsheadbucks.com
www.nagsheadbucks.co.uk

AA Rosette for Culinary Excellence
AA 4 Star Inn
AA Pick of the Pubs
"Food Pub of the Year" – The Publican Regional Award

The Nags Head in Great Missenden, Buckinghamshire is a traditional 15th century country Inn and restaurant situated along the valley of the River Misbourne in the glorious Chiltern Hills.

Brought to you by the Michaels family, owners of the award-winning Bricklayers Arms in Flaunden, Hertfordshire, the newly refurbished Nags Head serves an Anglo French fusion menu. The Nags Head has now been awarded with its first "Rosette" for its "Culinary Excellence" and accredited in several guides including a Commendation Award in the Hardens Guide; chosen as "Pick of the Pubs" in the AA Pub Guide and a recommendation and on the front cover of the Michelins "Eating Out in Pubs" and the much coveted "Michelin Guide".

The Nags Head was recently featured in the movie, Mr Fantastic Fox as it was an old favourite of children's author, Roald Dahl. You can also see executive head chef, Claude Paillet cook on Sky TV channel, Planet Food, at the Nags Head, cooking the great Sunday roast. If you miss one of the repeats, you can view it on 'YouTube'.

Dining guests will receive a warm welcome at the newly refurbished Nags Head. It has still kept all of its original features, including a large inglenook fireplace and low old oak beams, and many new features including a new bar and stylish new furnishings throughout.

Now graded as an AA 4 star Inn, there are half a dozen new double and twin bedrooms, all beautifully refurbished with bath or shower ensuites After a rested night's sleep, you'll find a hearty breakfast waiting for you in the morning.

Food is our passion; we use only the finest produce when available because we know it makes a difference and wherever possible, we source from local farms and suppliers. We believe in giving good value for money and serve only the finest quality food, so you can be assured of an excellent meal, time and time again. On the lunch and evening menus, you'll find favourites, such as home smoked fishes; mixed and wild mushroom feuillette; our famous 21 day aged Bedfordshire Fillet Steaks with a selection of sauces along with a great steak and kidney ale pie and local game. Fresh fish dishes are sourced according to market availability and change on a daily basis.

Don't miss out on our Sunday roasts where you'll find locally supplied fresh produce and mouthwatering puddings, along with an extensive award winning wine list to suit all tastes, as well as a selection of local ales.

Our bar is a great place to relax in front of the open fireplace and in the summer months you can enjoy a drink or meal in our delightful garden with attractive views of rolling hills of the Chilterns.

THE FOODIE GUIDE
Diner Review
"The steak is the best I have ever tasted."

Food service times:
Mon-Sat 12.00 pm - 2.30 pm & 6.30 - 9.30 pm
Sun 12.00 pm - 3.30 pm & 6.30pm - 8.30 pm

£5

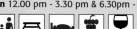

Award winning local chef Dan Cameron has opened his long awaited modern European restaurant, Cameron's Brasserie, in the historic coaching town of Stony Stratford.

This 40 seater restaurant situated in Odell's Yard offers a bright, airy and relaxed place to eat and drink in a great location. The walled courtyard offers further seating, perfect for those warmer months.

With Dan's emphasis on fresh, innovative food and his fine attention to both quality and detail, it's exactly what the town of Stony Stratford needed.

The Brasserie is open from 9.00 am until 10.00 pm, Tuesday to Saturday and until 3.00 pm on Sunday, which makes it the perfect place to meet up with friends or family for that morning coffee or light lunch. Cameron's offer a seasonal à la carte menu for lunch and dinner.

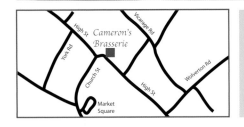

Food service times:
Tue - Sat 12.00 pm - 2.30 p.m. & 6.30 pm - 9.00 pm
Sun 12.00 pm - 3.00 pm
Drinks and coffees are served at all times.

CAMERON'S
BRASSERIE

5 Odells Yard
High Street
Stony Stratford
Milton Keynes MK11 1AQ
Tel: 01908 568000
Email: info@camerons-brasserie.co.uk
www.camerons-brasserie.co.uk

THE FOODIE GUIDE
Diner Review

"Delicious food, creatively presented – a wonderful addition to Stony Stratford."

Red Lion
COUNTRY HOTEL

Wavendon Road, Salford, Milton Keynes MK17 8AZ
Tel: 01908 583117
Email: info@redlionhotel.eu
www.redlionhotel.eu

The Red Lion in Salford Village has been in the hands of Bob and Pauline Sapsford for 23 years and has in that time been a pub/restaurant that has consistently delivered a friendly, traditional pub/dining experience.

It's a traditional country inn with log fires, a huge beer garden and six letting rooms. Recently refurbished with a fresh new look but has managed to keep its cosy country pub feel.

The extensive menu has something to suit all tastes, occasions and budgets with top quality steak meals, seafood and chicken dishes alongside a great selection of light meals and snacks. There are spicy and classic dishes and a fair selection for vegetarians too. And for wine and ale lovers they have achieved 'Wine Pub of the Year' awards nationaly and locally with Charles Wells and have been in the Good Beer Guide for 20 years.

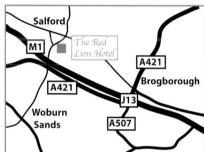

Food service times:
Mon-Sat 12.00 pm - 2.00 pm & 6.30 pm - 10.00 pm
Sun 12.00 pm - 2.30 pm & 6.30 pm - 9.00 pm

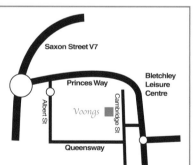

Voongs

1-2 Woodward House
Cambridge Street
Bletchley
MK2 2TH
Tel: 01908 370292

You must try it to believe it.

Food service times:
Mon Closed all day Monday except Bank Holidays
Tue-Fri 12.00 pm - 2.00 pm & 6.00 pm - 10.00 pm
Sat 6.00 pm - 10.00 pm
Sun 12.00 pm - 2.00 pm (Special Buffet)

The Three Tuns

57 Main Road
Biddenham
Bedfordshire
MK40 4BD
Tel: 01234 354847
Email: info@thethreetunsbiddenham.co.uk
www.thethreetunsbiddenham.co.uk

THE FOODIE GUIDE
Diner Review

"Very talented use of ingredients, loved every course here."

Situated in the beautiful backwater which is Biddenham, the Three Tuns has recently undergone a change of ownership together with an extensive refurbishment by Chef Chris Smith. Trained by the late Peter Chandler of Paris House, Chris then spent a number of years working alongside Jean Christophe Novelli progressing further by gaining 2 AA Rosettes in 2010.

Chris is passionate when it comes to sourcing the very best in seasonal produce with much supplied locally. Everything from sauces to ice cream is prepared on site. Adapting many traditional dishes to fit the modern English menu and with an excellent choice of daily specials and bar meals there is something for everyone.

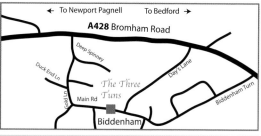

← To Newport Pagnell   To Bedford →
A428 Bromham Road
Deep Spinney
Duck End Ln
Day's Lane
The Three Tuns
Gold Ln
Main Rd
Biddenham Turn
Biddenham

Food service times:
Mon - Sat 12.00 pm - 2.30 pm & 6.00 pm - 9.30 pm
Sun 12.00 pm - 4.00 pm
Bar is open Monday to Sunday 12.00 pm - 11.30 pm

Bedfordshire   eating out   Bedfordshire

George Street
Woburn
Bedfordshire
MK17 9PX
Tel: 01525 290441
Fax: 01525 290432
Email: inn@woburn.co.uk
www.woburn.co.uk/inn

OLIVIER'S
RESTAURANT
AT THE INN AT WOBURN

Two AA rosettes
for fine food

Olivier's Restaurant at The Inn at Woburn offers a stylish and relaxed setting to enjoy the very best of English and continental dining.

Owned and managed by the historic Woburn estate, Olivier's Restaurant at The Inn at Woburn is situated in the heart of the Georgian village of Woburn.

With two AA Rosettes, the restaurant's reputation continues to flourish under the auspices of Executive Chef Olivier Bertho who provides a superb menu of contemporary French and British cuisine, all served with flair and imagination. An extensive and carefully selected wine list from around the globe perfectly complements the menus.

We also offer a range of daily specials and often celebrate special occasions with one-off dishes for lunch or dinner. In addition, we perpetuate the Woburn tradition of afternoon tea, which is said to have been started by Duchess Anna Maria, wife of the 7th Duke of Bedford in the 1840's when she served delicate sandwiches, cakes and biscuits in the Blue Drawing Room at Woburn Abbey.

The Tavistock Bar and Lounge at The Inn provides a welcoming and comfortable spot to relax and linger with pre-dinner drinks or after dinner coffee to make the most of your visit.

For further details of our menus, wine list and dining events, please visit the Woburn website: www.woburn.co.uk/inn.

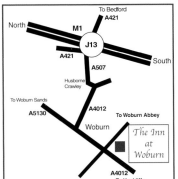

The Inn at Woburn

THE FOODIE GUIDE
Diner Review

"Extremely high standards for cuisine and service and a truly beautiful location."

Chez Jerome

26 Church Street
Dunstable
Bedfordshire
LU5 4RU
Tel: 01582 603310
Email: info@chezjerome.co.uk
www.chezjerome.co.uk

THE FOODIE GUIDE
Diner Review

"Warm, welcoming atmosphere and delicious food, with creatively designed menus."

Chez Jerome is owned and run by husband and wife team Jerome and Lina Dehoux. Situated in Dunstable this French restaurant is renound for it's impressive dishes. Head chef Jerome has worked in kitchens all over the world including Switzerland, Luxembourg as well as his native France where he was sous chef in the Michelin star "La Toque Blanche".

The 15th century timber framed building together with its décor certainly sets the mood for experiencing Jerome's superb skill as a chef. Most of his ingredients he sources locally, its freshness and quality is apparent in the taste. The layout of the restaurant is ideal and even allows for small closed off areas where diners can feel secluded.

With ample parking a few steps away and friendly, knowledgeable staff serving first rate dishes ensures Chez Jerome's ongoing popularity and a really nice touch is that they will open early for you if you wish to eat before going to the theatre or cinema.

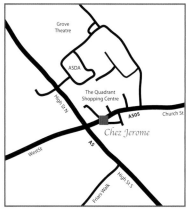

Food service times:

Mon-Fri 12.00 pm - 2.30 pm & 6.00 pm - 10.00 pm
Sat 12.00 pm - 2.30 pm & 6.00 pm - 10.30 pm
Sun 12.00 pm - 3.00 pm

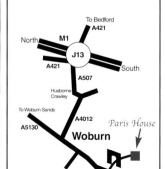

Food service times:
Tue Dinner to **Sun** Lunch

To Bedford
A421
North **M1**
J13 South
A421
A507
Husborne
Crawley
To Woburn Sands
A4012
Paris House
A5130
Woburn
A4012
A5 Hockliffe

Paris House
Woburn Park
Woburn
Bedfordshire
MK17 9QP
Tel: 01525 290692
Email: info@parishouse.co.uk
www.parishouse.co.uk

Set in 22 acres of stunning parkland on the historic Woburn Estate, Paris House is Bedfordshire's only Michelin-starred restaurant.

At the helm of the kitchen is award-winning chef Phil Fanning, who together with his team of talented chefs, blends modern culinary techniques with the finest local produce to create fine dining interpretations of classic dishes. The restaurant's "Retro" menus are designed to evoke memories of the past. Don't be surprised to see a Bedfordshire Clanger, Coq au Vin, Rum Baba or banana split on the menu!

THE FOODIE GUIDE
Diner Review

"Absolutely what you would expect from this talented team. The food and service are outstanding."

For the real foodies dining on the Chef's Table offers an unforgettable culinary experience. Sitting directly opposite the pass, you'll witness all the action of the service as well as the Head Chef plating each dish to be served in the restaurant. For those extra special occasions Paris House also offers a Private Dining Suite allowing you to celebrate with family and friends or entertain corporate clients.

Bedfordshire **eating out** *Bedfordshire*

The Kings Head

Ivinghoe
Leighton Buzzard
Bedfordshire
LU7 9EB
Tel: 01296 668388
Fax: 01296 668107
Email: info@kingsheadivinghoe.co.uk
www.kingsheadivinghoe.co.uk

THE FOODIE GUIDE
Diner Review

"A great restaurant with wonderfully cooked and imaginative dishes."

The Kings Head is situated in the very heart of the picturesque village of Ivinghoe, on the Beds, Bucks and Herts borders. This ivy covered building dates back to times when quality and service went hand in hand and happily it still exists here to this day.

We pride ourselves on good old fashioned service and serious professionalism. Georges de Maison's passion for quality food, meticulous attention to detail and impeccable service ensures that your dining experience will be memorable if not unique. Soft candlelight and shimmering silverware complement the restaurants already inviting ambience.

Chef de Cuisine Jonathan O'Keeffe is famed for his skillfully prepared eclectic menus. Only the very best and freshest of produce is used with much of this sourced locally. After lunch or perhaps before dinner, why not take a stroll around the village and visit the windmill. If the weather is inclement take the opportunity sit back in one of our comfy chairs, order your favourite aperitif and let the world go by! Alternatively, take a few moments to explore over 50 original works of art which adorn the walls.

A Banqueting Suite is available for conferences and private dining for up to 40 guests. For larger functions and weddings, marquees can be put in the beautiful walled garden.

We promise a warm welcome and look forward to seeing you soon.

To Luton & Dunstable
To Leighton Buzzard
B488
The KingsHead
B489
Ivinghoe
Whipsnade
B489
A4146
A41(M)
B488
Tring
B4506
To Berkhamsted

Vouchers valid Mon-Thur for dinner only 10% **DC**

Food service times:
Mon-Sat 12.00 pm - 2.15 pm & 7.00 pm - 9.15 pm
Sun 12.00 pm - 2.15 pm

Galloway's

Aberdeen House
22-23 Market Place
Woburn
Bedfordshire
MK17 9PZ
Tel: 01525 290496
www.gallowayswoburn.com

THE FOODIE GUIDE
Diner Review

"Extremely good food and exceptional service combined with a lively atmosphere"

'Party bookings and pre-booked lunches are welcomed'

Galloway's is a family run restaurant providing a relaxed informal atmosphere in a Grade II listed building in the heart of the historic village of Woburn.

Tuesday is our Pasta, Steak and Fish evening and Wednesday to Saturday we offer an à la carte menu which changes regularly, using only the best fresh produce. On Sunday we add our traditional roast selection to the menu for lunchtime service and we always have delicious vegetarian dishes.

Open for Lunch and Dinner service during December. We will be celebrating our 17th Anniversary in November.

THE FOODIE AWARD
2009
Bedfordshire
winner

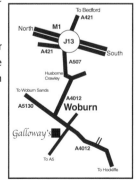

Food service times:
Tue-Sat 6.30 pm - 10.00 pm (last orders)
Sun 12.00 pm - 3.00 pm

Vouchers not accepted on Saturdays

ST. HELENA
RESTAURANT

High Street, Elstow
Bedfordshire
MK42 9XP
Tel: 01234 344848
www.sthelenarestaurant.com

THE FOODIE GUIDE
Diner Review

"Always excellent food, talented and imaginative use of ingredients and a very friendly welcome."

St Helena is set in what was the birth village of the famous Christian writer John Bunyan. Converted from a private 17th century house it sits in a lovely walled garden not far from Elstow's picturesque village green.

Four separate dining areas greet you upon entering through the garden, culminating in a contemporary garden room. Beyond this can be found a small walled seating area heavily scented in the summer with fragrant roses, lavender, honeysuckle and rosemary. Fine paintings, beautiful mirrors and antiques give the interior a tranquil and peaceful feel during quiet midweek periods with a much busier feel at the weekend.

Brothers-in-law Raffaele and Franco offer an appealing classic and contemporary menu with Italian/French influence. Over 300 wines can be found on an interesting wine list which includes many in the fine and rare bracket!

Meats including aged beef and rare breed pork or game are regular dishes, along with the ever popular St Helena fillet stuffed with stilton. Scallops, crab and oysters come from Bigbury Bay near Salcombe in Devon along with Cornish lobster sometimes served as "Posh Fish & Chips".

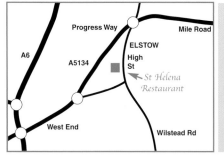

Progress Way
Mile Road
A6
ELSTOW
A5134
High St
St Helena Restaurant
West End
Wilstead Rd

Food service times:
Sunday & Monday Closed all day
Tue 7.00 pm - 9.00 pm (last orders)
Wed-Thur 12.15 pm - 1.00 pm (last orders)
& 7.00 pm - 9.00 pm (last orders)
Fri-Sat 7.00 pm - 9.00 pm (last orders)

THE FOODIE AWARD 2008 winner

lunch   dinner

Cornfields Restaurant

Wilden Road, Colmworth, Bedfordshire MK44 2NJ
Tel: 01234 378990
Email: reservations@cornfieldsrestaurant.co.uk
www.cornfieldsrestaurant.co.uk

THE FOODIE GUIDE
Diner Review

"Really good food, well presented and attentive service."

A Breath of Fresh Air

A fresh food restaurant with five bedrooms located in peaceful countryside only fifteen minutes from Bedford town centre.

We offer traditional but non stuffy hospitality and service with a friendly enthusiastic hand picked team serving freshly prepared food from local producers where possible, cooked to order at sensible prices in an atmosphere that complements our food.

Our menus are constantly changing offering a varied and interesting selection of Fresh Fish, Meat, Game and Vegetarian choices.

Once a village inn, the main building dates back to the 17th century and is a Grade Two listed building which still retains its original oak beams and inglenook fireplace with bread oven. We have two dining rooms and a lounge with bar for pre or after dinner drinks. The larger of our dining rooms opens out on to a spacious sun deck with views out over the fields, which also has a fully enclosed marquee offering

another venue for group or party bookings. Either of our dining rooms can be used for small weddings, private functions or conferences.

In addition to our Restaurant we have a choice of five spacious bedrooms set in our peaceful gardens. Each individually furnished offering a place to unwind and recharge after a busy day if on a business trip, or if on leisure to just relax with good food and hospitality.

We look forward to welcoming you.

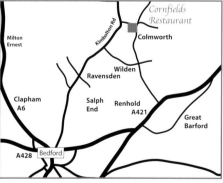

Food service times:
Mon-Sat 6.30 pm - 9.30 pm
Sun 12.00 pm - 1.45 pm

eating out

Bedfordshire

Bedfordshire

The Prince of Wales

24 Bedford Street, Ampthill, Bedfordshire MK45 2NB
Tel: 01525 840504
Fax: 01525 840574
Email: ricksbar1@aol.com
www.princeofwales-ampthill.com

THE FOODIE GUIDE
Diner Review

"Friendly service and the food and atmosphere were excellent."

Welcome to the Prince of Wales, where freshly prepared quality food and wines meets informality and a relaxing atmosphere in a unique but comfortable setting. The Prince of Wales is a traditional red brick town inn, where the emphasis is on hospitality - from the welcoming ambience and the attentive service to the quality of the dining experience. The Prince of Wales delights with its individually designed surroundings and consideration to detail. Fresh flowers, new oak and flagstone flooring throughout combine to make the perfect setting to relax over coffee or drinks, have lunch or dinner, or enjoy al fresco dining in the garden.

The award winning Prince of Wales has now been included nationally in The Good Pub Guide for the past four years including 2012. We pride ourselves on only using the finest locally sourced produce which is lovingly prepared daily by our team of experienced chefs.

Families with children are welcome at any time of the week and depending on what they eat we charge accordingly. Food allergies are taken very seriously by the chefs at The Prince of Wales, we can cater for gluten, nut and lactose free. Please advise us upon booking and we will accommodate all your dietary requirements. We are also dog friendly so after a long walk in Ampthill Park you can rest and enjoy a meal in our welcoming bar with your dog.

The Prince of Wales has the perfect atmosphere for every occasion. Private parties of up to 100 people are catered for, the restaurant is ideal for wedding receptions, banquets, parties or any special occasion. Alternatively, we also offer outside catering. We look forward to welcoming you at The Prince of Wales.

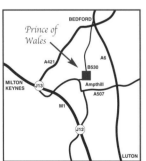

Vouchers valid Monday to Thursday evenings only

Opening times:
Mon-Sat 11.00 am - 11.00 pm
Sun 12.00 pm - 4.00 pm

eating out

CHEZ MUMTAJ
Modern French-Asian Dining
Restaurant & Saffron Lounge Champagne Bar

136-142 London Road
St Albans
Hertfordshire
AL1 1PQ
Tel: 01727 800033
Email: info@chezmumtaj.com
www.chezmumtaj.com

THE FOODIE GUIDE
Diner Review

"The flavours are amazing; truly beautiful, fresh and creative food."

Winner of St. Albans Retailer of The Year 2011
Winner of St. Albans Best Restaurant of The Year 2011
Top Ten AA Rosette Academy's Hall of Fame Award
Top 4 Best in Britain Award by Mood Food Magazine 2011
Independent Newspaper Top Ten Best Asian Restaurant 2010-2011

Chez Mumtaj is designed to impart the essence of stunning French and Asian cuisine, showcasing evolved modern dishes from India, France, Thailand, China and Malaysia for the discerning palate. The philosophy at Chez Mumtaj is to be innovative, progressive, persistent and passionate with cuisine and service.

Award winning Executive Chef Chad Rahman has created an eclectic menu depicting a diversity of traditional dishes with a contemporary twist. The menu encompasses a wide range of tastes and flavours journeying through South East Asia and Europe incorporating nuances of Pan Asian and European cuisines. Menus change regularly using only the finest and freshest seasonal ingredients.

For private or corporate events of 8 to 16 guests, there is a private dining room. They can co-ordinate and create a menu to suit your requirements so that the event is successful, bringing attention to detail, care and hospitality. The aim is to create a unique and memorable experience, tailored to your needs.

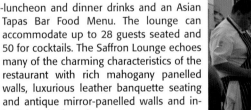

The Saffron Lounge offers an ideal space for pre-luncheon and dinner drinks and an Asian Tapas Bar Food Menu. The lounge can accommodate up to 28 guests seated and 50 for cocktails. The Saffron Lounge echoes many of the charming characteristics of the restaurant with rich mahogany panelled walls, luxurious leather banquette seating and antique mirror-panelled walls and in-built booths for privacy.

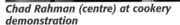

Chad Rahman (centre) at cookery demonstration

Voucher not valid Friday to Saturday.
Accepted from à la carte menu only.
Minimum of 2 courses (Starter & Main)
£5

Food service times:
Tue-Sun 12.00 pm - 2.30 pm & 6.00 pm - 11.00 pm
The Saffron Lounge opening times:
Tue-Sun 6.00 pm - 11.00 pm

The Vine House Hotel & Restaurant

100 High Street, Paulerspury
Northamptonshire, NN12 7NA
Tel: 01327 811267
Fax: 01327 811309
Email: info@vinehousehotel.com
www.vinehousehotel.com

Multi award winning

Dedicated Foodies Chef Marcus and Host Julie Springett are celebrating 21 years and about to launch a book. Steeped in history this place moves with the times. They love sharing all that is great about their multi award winning restaurant with rooms above. Located just off the A5 at Paulerspury, near Silverstone home of motor racing, Towcester for horse racing, county towns Northampton and Buckingham, shoppers' havens Milton Keynes and Bicester Village.

THE FOODIE GUIDE
Diner Review

"Perfection on a plate! Would highly recommend."

Here it really is all about the food. Passionately presented, packed with flavour and interesting marriages that really work for affordable top taste experiences whatever the season. Locally sourced ingredients including rare breed meats excite the taste buds providing a fusion of traditional English and modern continental cuisine with a twist. From only £30.95 for 3 courses, £27.50 for 2 courses per head, expect informal dining with crisp linen table cloths and award winning food.

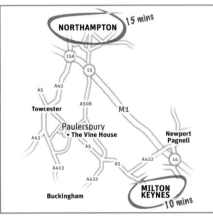

Food service times:
Lunch **Tue-Sat** 12.30 pm - 1.45 pm
Dinner **Mon-Sun** 6.30 pm - 10.00 pm
Special openings on Sunday for events and stopovers / residents

£5

Whittlebury Hall Hotel & Spa
Whittlebury
Nr Towcester
Northamptonshire
NN12 8QH
Tel: 0845 400 0001
Fax: 01327 857867
Email: reservations@whittleburyhall.co.uk
www.whittleburyhall.co.uk

Two AA rosettes
for fine food

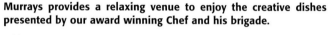

Murrays provides a relaxing venue to enjoy the creative dishes presented by our award winning Chef and his brigade.

With an ever increasing interest in food the Murrays menu, which changes regularly, provides our guests with the perfect opportunity to taste the latest blends of flavours and ingredients to make your visit to Murrays at Whittlebury Hall truly memorable.

Food service times:
Tue - Sat 7.00 pm - 9.30 pm

We are proud to use the finest carefully sourced quality seasonal and local ingredients. Our Head Chef and the team use their creativity to bring you simple and elegant dishes. Our style could be described as modern British with international influences and classical based cookery, with contemporary twists and touches. All food, from the appetisers to the desserts are produced in-house from carefully created recipes, no dish is left to chance. With our culinary confidence, imagination and passion, your Murrays experience is sure to be a memorable one.

Whilst relaxing in the lounge and during dinner you can reminisce on the F1 commentary years of Murray Walker as we display a collection of photographs with F1 celebrities and also display some unique anecdotes of his memorable career.

For more details go to www.whittleburyhall.co.uk/murrays or to book your fine dining experience call 0845 400 0001.

To begin - **TEA SMOKED DUCK** with fennel, beetroot, pistachio and star anise

Main dish - **35 DAYS DRY AGED BEEF** fillet with onions, mushrooms and horseradish

To finish - **CHOCOLATE AND TONKA BEAN** chocolate mousse with tonka bean ice cream

CROMWELL COTTAGE

1 High Street
Kislingbury
Northamptonshire
NN7 4AG
Tel: 01064 830288
www.thecromwellcottagekislingbury.co.uk

Before word got around, the Cromwell Cottage was one of Kislingbury's best-kept secrets. The cosy pub and restaurant serves well kept cask ales, quaffable wines and tasty, unpretentious pub food, lovingly prepared by local chef Jules.

The beautifully restored building was once known as 'the restaurant over the bridge' and has played host to various shenanigans over the years, most notably when Oliver Cromwell used it as a hideout from marauding Royalists.

Food served all day:
Mon-Sat 12.00 pm - 10.00 pm
Sun 11.30 am - 9.30 pm

Opening times:
Mon-Sat 11.30 am - 11.00 pm
Sun 11.30 am - 10.30 pm

THE FOODIE GUIDE
Diner Review
"Stylish interior and well cooked food, especially enjoyed the fish."

Roade House
restaurant & hotel

16 High Street
Roade
Northants
NN7 2NW
Tel: 01604 863372
Fax: 01604 862421
Email: info@roadehousehotel.co.uk
www.roadehousehotel.co.uk

The Roade House restaurant has been owned by Chris and Sue Kewley for nearly 29 years. For most of that time it has been listed in The Good Food Guide as well as the Michelin, Harden and AA Restaurant Guides.

The building was originally a local village pub, The White Hart before it was converted into a restaurant. In 1997 an adjoining cottage was incorporated to create 10 guest bedrooms. Sue runs front of house and Chris is in charge of the kitchen.

Although the menu is small it is made using fresh, top quality and predominantly seasonal ingredients cooked to order. The Roade House provides an informal and relaxed atmosphere.

In addition to being an excellent venue for romantic dinners, business meetings or just a casual night out, a wide variety of functions are also catered for, from weddings to Golden wedding anniversaries, significant birthdays, retirement dinners and so on. Their extensive experience of organising and running functions means they are happy to produce tailored menus and for larger events offer exclusive use of the premises.

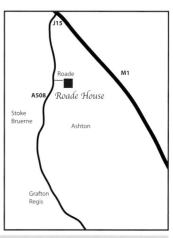

Food service times:
Mon-Fri 12.30 pm - 1.45 pm & 7.00 pm - 9.30 pm
Sat 7.00 pm - 9.30 pm
Sun 12 noon - 2.00 pm

Northamptonshire eating out Northamptonshire

Northampton Road
Grafton Regis
Northants NN12 7SR
Tel: 01908 542123
www.pubgraftonregis.com

THE FOODIE GUIDE
Diner Review

"Delicious homemade food and a great atmosphere."

The White Hart is a stone under thatch 16th Century building located in the small village of Grafton Regis and has been owned by the Drake family for over 16 years.

Owner chef Alan and his team prepare all their dishes on the premises freshly and daily. The menu changes frequently depending on what fresh produce is currently available. The fish arrives daily from Grimsby supplied by Keith Wright who delivers fresh fish in the area, providing a friendly door to door service for many villages. The meat which is mainly British is supplied by Bookers of Great Billing. Alan's insistence for using only the freshest ingredients possible ensures an ever changing menu, therefore the Specials Board changes daily.

Andy takes care of front of house and is constantly trying to improve on what they have. The concept at the pub now offers one large menu in all areas so you can enjoy your meal in the air conditioned restaurant or in the traditional lounge bar area and weather permitting their wonderful garden which has a large patio area.

Having this much commitment brings rewards having been awarded by Green King Brewery the

title of "Catering Pub of the Year" winning first place from over 700 other entrants. Little wonder then that their board outside thanks over 19,000 diners that have visited them this past year.

As you would imagine, the restaurant is very popular, comfortably seating between 26 and 29 so you are strongly advised to book your table to avoid disappointment, and for that special occasion you can book the entire restaurant providing the numbers are a minimum of 24.

Food service times:
Mon Closed
Tue-Sat 12.00 pm - 2.00 pm & 6.00 pm - 9.30 pm
Sun 12.00 pm - 2.00 pm & 7.00 pm - 9.00 pm

Vouchers accepted Tue-Thurs only

Bar   Restaurant

Franks
STEAKHOUSE

176 Wellingborough Road
Northampton
Northamptonshire
NN1 4DZ
Tel: 01604 949804
www.frankssteakhouse.co.uk

Franks Steakhouse is owned by Tom Hewer and managed by Sophie Smith. Together with head chef Oli Butel and the rest of the team they will ensure you have an enjoyable time.

They opened their doors in October 2011 with the aim of serving fantastic locally sourced food in a traditional yet contemporary atmosphere. Steaks are cooked over a Josper Oven and served on wooden boards accompanied by homemade rough cut chips and side dishes. The Josper Oven is the preferred choice by many top London Steakhouses. They cook at much higher temperatures – 650/700°F – which seals in the flavour and gives that traditional barbecued taste which we all know and love.

They serve a fantastic range of steaks, with cuts from Sirloin to 32oz Cote de Beouf. There is also fresh fish, chicken, and vegetarian dishes, accompanied by fine wines and excellent desserts. A fine selection of Bibendum wines are available; 125 ml, 175 ml, carafe or bottle, something to suit all tastes. The aim is to provide local produce; steaks are sourced from Church Farm, Overstone and vegetables are supplied by Whites Nurseries, Earls Barton. Bitter from Nobby's Brewery, Guilsborough is on offer as well as a range of their own ice cream in the homemade dessert menu.

They are also deservedly proud to be finalists in the Northamptonshire Food & Drink Awards for Chef and Restaurant of the year. In May 2012, Franks opened a sister restaurant, Franks Hamburger House which can also be found in the Wellingborough Road, Northampton.

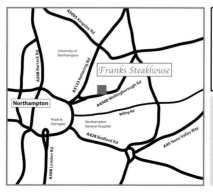

THE FOODIE GUIDE
Diner Review

"This is the place to visit if you want the best in steaks. However, there is plenty of other choice on the menu too."

Food service times:
Mon 6.30 pm - 10.00 pm
Tue - Sat 11.00 am - 2.30 pm & 6.30 pm - 10.00 pm
Sun 12.00 pm - 3.00 pm & 6.30 pm - 10.00 pm

THE OLD CROWN

1 Stoke Road
Ashton
Northampton
Northamptonshire
NN7 2JN
Tel: 01604 862268
Email: bex@theoldcrownashton.co.uk
www.theoldcrownashton.co.uk

THE FOODIE GUIDE
Diner Review

"This is a favourite restaurant of ours, always good honest food with lots of choice on offer."

The small village of Ashton is just a stones throw from the A508 midway between Northampton and Milton Keynes. Chef Ian and his wife Bex took over this lovely dining pub just a couple of years ago and have already made massive changes, which include new menus as well as good ales. Not surprising then that their reputation for good food is gradually spreading further afield.

The Old Crown is the heart of the village and is a warm and welcoming inn with a lovely safe garden to relax in the summer sunshine. Winter times the cosy interior is a great place to just sit back and watch the world go by.

As a chef and owner Ian ensures that all his produce is sourced locally wherever possible and meals prepared freshly in his kitchen. He sets high standards and expects his kitchen team to maintain them. You can expect a good choice from the menu, starters such as Fresh Crab with Gazpacho and Cucumber Sauce, Deep Fried Squid with Aioli or Grilled Goats Cheese with a Pine Nut and Herb Crust. Main courses may include Twice Cooked Pigs Cheeks with Parsnip Mash, Red Wine and Smoky Bacon, Local Pork Sausages with Bubble and Squeak and Cider Gravy or Honey Roast Duck Breast with Dauphinoise Potato Gratin. If you have a sweet tooth the dessert menu will delight with some delicious traditional favourites.

Front of house, wife Bex is there to welcome you and ensure your visit is a memorable one. All well-behaved dogs are also very welcome.

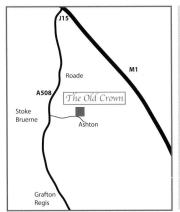

Opening times:
Tue-Fri 12.00 pm to 3.00 pm & 6.00 pm - 11.30 pm
Sat 12.00 pm - 11.30 pm
Sun 12.00 pm - 10.30 pm

Food service times:
Tue-Fri 12.00 pm - 3.00 pm & 6.00 pm - 9.30 pm
Sat 12.00 pm - 9.30 pm
Sun 12.00 pm - 6.00 pm

The Alford Arms

34

Frithsden
Nr Hemel Hempstead
Hertfordshire
HP1 3DD
Tel: 01442 864480
Email: info@alfordarmsfrithsden.co.uk
www.alfordarmsfrithsden.co.uk

The Angel Restaurant

35

47 Bicester Road, Long Crendon, Aylesbury, Bucks HP18 9EE
Tel: 01844 208268 **Email:** info@angelrestaurant.co.uk
www.angelrestaurant.co.uk

Auberge du Lac

36

Brocket Hall
Welwyn
Hertfordshire
AL8 7XG
Tel: 01707 368888
Email: aubergeevents@brocket-hall.co.uk
www.aubergedulac.co.uk

The Barge Inn

37

15 Newport Road, Woolstone, Milton Keynes MK15 0AE
Tel: 01908 233841
www.vintageinn.co.uk

The Bedford Arms

38

High Street, Oakley, Beds MK43 7RH
Tel: 01234 822280
www.bedfordarmsoakley.co.uk

The Bell Hotel & Inn

39

21 Bedford Street, Woburn, Beds MK17 9QB
Tel: 01525 290280
www.bellinn-woburn.co.uk

The Bell Inn

40

Main Street, Beachampton, Bucks MK19 6DX
Tel: 01908 563861 **Email:** info@thebellrestaurant.co.uk
www.thebellrestaurant.co.uk

The Belvedere

41

Ardmore House Hotel, 54 Lemsford Road, St Albans, Herts AL1 3PR
Tel: 01727 859313
www.ardmorehousehotel.co.uk

The Birch

42

20 Newport Road
Woburn
Buckinghamshire
MK17 9HX
Tel: 01525 290295
Email: info@birchwoburn.com
www.birchwoburn.com

The Black Horse

43

Windmill Road
Fulmer
Bucks
SL3 6HD
Tel: 01753 663183
Email: info@blackhorsefulmer.co.uk
www.blackhorsefulmer.co.uk

The Black Horse

44

Ireland
Shefford
Bedfordshire
SG17 5QL
Tel: 01462 811398
Email: info@blackhorseireland.com
www.blackhorseireland.com

The Boat Inn

45

Stoke Bruerne, Northants, NN12 7SB
Tel: 01604 862428 **Email:** enquiries@boatinn.co.uk
www.boatinn.co.uk

The Boot at Sarratt

46

The Green, Sarratt, Rickmansworth, Herts WD3 6BL
Tel: 01923 262247 **Email:** thebootsarratt@gmail.com
www.thebootsarratt.com

The Brampton Halt

47

Pitsford Road, Chapel Brampton, Northants NN6 8BA
Tel: 01604 842676 **Email:** bramptonhalt@mcmanuspub.co.uk
www.mcmanuspub.co.uk

Brasserie Blanc

48

Chelsea House, 301 Avebury Blvd, Central Milton Keynes, Bucks MK9 2GA
Tel: 01908 546590
www.brasserieblanc.com

more reader recommendations

69 **The Hillside Restaurant & Patisserie**
54 High Street, Wheathampstead, Herts AL4 8AR
Tel: 01582 833111 **Email:** reservations@thehillside.co.uk
www.thehillside.co.uk

70 **The Hopping Hare**
18 Hopping Hill Gardens, Duston, Northants NN5 6PF
Tel: 01604 580090 **Email:** info@hoppinghare.com
www.hoppinghare.com

71  **Horse & Jockey**
Church End
Ravensden
Bedfordshire MK44 2RR
Tel: 01234 772319
www.horseandjockey.info

72 **Jacoby's Bar & Restaurant**
Churchgate House, 15 West Street, Ware, Herts SG12 9EE
Tel: 01920 469181 **Email:** info@jacobys.co.uk
www.jacobys.co.uk

73 **Just 32**
32 Sun Street, Hitchin, Herts SG5 1AH
Tel: 01462 455666 **Email:** david@just32.com
www.just32.com

74 **Kashu**
9 Hatfield Road, St Albans, Herts AL1 3RR
Tel: 01727 854436 **Email:** info@kashu.co.uk
www.kashu.co.uk

75 **La Dolce Vita**
18 Hopping Hill Gardens, Duston, Northants NN5 6PF
Tel: 01604 580090 **Email:** info@hoppinghare.com
www.hoppinghare.com

76 **La Stalla Restaurant**
The Green Man, The Green, Clophill, Beds MK45 4AD
Tel: 01525 860352 **Email:** info@lastallarestaurant.co.uk
www.lastallarestaurant.co.uk

77 **Lussmanns**
Waxhouse Gate, St Albans, Herts AL3 4EW
Tel: 01727 851941 **Email:** chris@lussmanns.com
www.lussmanns.com

78 **The Lytton Arms**
Park Lane, Old Knebworth, Herts SG3 6QB
Tel: 01438 812312 **Email:** info@lyttonarms.co.uk
www.lyttonarms.co.uk

79 **The Narrow Boat**
A5 Watling Street, Stowe Hill, Weedon, Northants NN7 4RZ
Tel: 01327 340333
www.narrowboatatweedon.co.uk

80  **The Oak Restaurant**
The Pendley Manor Hotel
Cow Lane
Tring, Herts HP23 5QY
Tel: 01442 891891
Email: sales@pendley-manor.co.uk
www.pendley-manor.co.uk

81  **The Old Queens Head**
Hammersley Lane
Penn
High Wycombe, Bucks
HP10 8EY
Tel: 01494 813371
Email: info@oldqueensheadpenn.co.uk
www.oldqueensheadpenn.co.uk

82 **The Old Swan**
58 High Street, Cheddington, Nr Leighton Buzzard, Beds LU7 0RQ
Tel: 01296 668226 **Email:** info@theoldswancheddington.co.uk
www.theoldswancheddington.co.uk

83 **The Olde Red Lion**
15 High Street, Kislingbury, Northants NN7 4AQ
Tel: 01604 830219
www.theolderedlion.net

84 **Orangery Restaurant**
Shendish Manor Hotel & Golf Club, London Rd, Apsley, Herts HP3 0AA
Tel: 01442 232220
www.shendish-manor.com

85 **The Plough Restaurant**
Kimbolton Road, Bolnhurst, Beds MK44 2EX
Tel: 01234 376274 **Email:** theplough@bolnhurst.com
www.bolnhurst.com

Prego
86
4 High St, Buckingham, MK18 1NT
Tel: 01280 821205 **Email:** mail@pregorestaurants.com
www.pregorestaurants.com

Prego
87
8 St John's St, Newport Pagnell, Bucks, MK16 0EP
Tel: 01908 217535 **Email:** mail@pregorestaurants.com
www.pregorestaurants.com

The Purple Goose
88
61 High Street, Woburn Sands, Bucks MK17 8QY
Tel: 01908 584385 **Email:** mail@thepurplegoose.co.uk
www.thepurplegoose.co.uk

The Red Chilli
89
9 High Street, Buckingham, Bucks MK18 1NT
Tel: 01280 822226
www.redchilligold.com

Redcoats Farmhouse Hotel & Restaurant
90
Redcoats Green, Nr Hitchin, Herts SG4 7JR
Tel: 01438 729500 **Email:** info@redcoats.co.uk
www.redcoats.co.uk

The Red Lion
91
36 Bridle Path, Brafield-on-the-Green, Northants NN7 1BP
Tel: 01604 890707 **Email:** theredlion@mcmanuspub.co.uk
www.theredlionbrafield.co.uk

The Red Lion
92
89 High Street, Yardley Hastings, Northants NN7 1ER
Tel: 01604 696210 **Email:** info@redlionatyardleyhastings.co.uk
www.redliionatyardleyhastings.co.uk

The Red Lion Hotel
93
Main Street, East Haddon, Northants NN6 8BU
Tel: 01604 770223 **Email:** nick@redlioneasthaddon.co.uk
www.redlioneasthaddon.co.uk

The Robin Hood
94
Clifton Reynes, Bucks MK46 5DR
Tel: 01234 711574
www.therobinhoodpub.co.uk

The Rose and Crown Bistro
95
4 Northampton Road, Yardley Hastings, Northants NN7 1EX
Tel: 01604 696276
www.roseandcrownbistro.co.uk

The Royal Oak
96
Frieth Road
Bovingdon Green
Nr Marlow
Bucks SL7 2JF
Tel: 01628 488611
Email: info@royaloakmarlow.co.uk
www.royaloakmarlow.co.uk

The Royal Oak
97
4 Biggleswade Road, Potton, Beds SG19 2LU
Tel: 01767 261888 **Email:** enquiries@theroyaloakpotton.co.uk
www.theroyaloakpotton.co.uk

The Royal Oak at Eydon
98
Lime Avenue, Eydon, Northants NN11 3PG
Tel: 01327 263167
www.theroyaloakateydon.co.uk

The Russell Arms
99
2 Chalkshires Road, Butlers Cross, Ellesborough, Bucks HP17 0TS
Tel: 01296 622618 **Email:** info@therussellarms.com
www.therussellarms.com

The Saracen's Head
100
Main Street, Little Brington, Northants NN7 4HS
Tel: 01604 770640 **Email:** info@yeoldesaracenshead.co.uk
www.thesaracensatbrington.co.uk

The Seafood Café
101
47-49 St Giles Street, Northampton, NN1 1JF
Tel: 01604 627989
www.theseafoodcafe.co.uk

The Silk Road
102
151 Grafton Gate East, Central Milton Keynes, Bucks MK9 1AE
Tel: 01908 200522 **Email:** enquiries@thesilkroadrestaurants.co.uk
www.thesilkroadrestaurants.co.uk

Spice of Bruerne
103
5 The Canalside, Stoke Bruerne, Northants NN12 7SB
Tel: 01604 863330 **Email:** mail@spiceofbruerne.co.uk
www.spiceofbruerne.com

The Stag Inn
104
The Green, Mentmore, Beds LU7 0QF
Tel: 01296 668423 **Email:** info@thestagmentmore.com
www.thestagmentmore.com

105 **St Michaels Manor**
Fishpool Street, St Albans, Herts AL3 4RY
Tel: 01727 864444
www.stmichaelsmanor.com

106 **The Stuffed Olive**
190 Wellingborough Road, Northampton NN1 4EB
Tel: 01604 631631
www.thestuffedolive.co.uk

107 **The Sun at Northaw**
Judges Hill, Northaw, Potters Bar, Herts EN6 4NL
Tel: 01707 655507 **Email:** info@thesunatnorthaw.co.uk
www.thesunatnorthaw.co.uk

108

The Swan Inn
Village Road
Denham
Bucks
UB9 5BH
Tel: 01895 832085
Email: info@swaninndenham.co.uk
www.swaninndenham.co.uk

109

The Swan
2 Wavendon Road
Salford
Bucks
MK17 8BD
Tel: 01908 281008
Email: swan@peachpubs.com
www.swansalford.co.uk

110 **The Swan at Lamport**
Harborough Road, Lamport, Northants NN6 9EZ
Tel: 01604 686555 **Email:** theswanlamport@mcmanuspub.co.uk
www.theswanlamport.co.uk

111 **The Tree at Cadmore**
Marlow Road, Cadmore End, High Wycombe, Bucks HP14 3PF
Tel: 01494 881183 **Email:** cadmore@treehotel.co.uk
www.cadmore.treehotel.co.uk

112 **The Vanilla Pod**
31 West Street, Marlow, Bucks SL7 2LS
Tel: 01628 898101
www.thevanillapod.co.uk

113 **The Walnut Tree Inn**
21 Station Road, Blisworth, Northants NN7 3DS
Tel: 01604 859551
www.walnut-tree.co.uk

114 **The Wharf**
Cornhill Lane, Bugbrooke, Northants NN7 3QB
Tel: 01604 832585 **Email:** rich@the-wharf.co.uk
www.the-wharf.co.uk

115 **White Hart**
54 High Street. Flore, Northants NN7 4LW
Tel: 01327 341748
www.whitehartflore.co.uk

116 **White Hart**
Ampthill Road, Maulden, Beds MK45 2DH
Tel: 01525 406118 **Email:** info@whitehartmaulden.com
www.whitehartsaladcart.com

117 **The White Hart**
Brook Lane, Flitton, Beds MK45 5EJ
Tel: 01525 862022 **Email:** philhale@btconnect.com
www.whitehartflitton.co.uk

118 **The White Horse**
White Horse Lane, Burnham Green, Nr Welwyn, Herts AL6 0HA
Tel: 01438 798100
www.whitehorseburnhamgreen.com

119 **The Windhover**
Brampton Lane, Chapel Brampton, Northampton NN6 8AA
Tel: 01604 847859
www.vintageinn.co.uk

120 **The Worlds End**
Ecton, Northants NN6 0QN
Tel: 01604 414521 **Email:** info@theworldsend.org
www.theworldsend.org

121 **Ye Olde Swan**
Newport Road, Woughton on the Green, Milton Keynes, Bucks MK6 3BS
Tel: 01908 679489 **Email:** reza.najafi@pubandkitchenco.com
www.pubandkitchenco.com

122 **The Zodiac Restaurant**
Hanbury Manor Hotel, Ware, Herts SG12 0SD
Tel: 01920 487722
www.marriott.co.uk

123 **ARTea Room**
Wakefield Country Courtyard, Potterspury, Northants NN12 7QX
Tel: 01327 810245
www.artearoom.co.uk

124 **The Barn Restaurant**
The Old Dairy Farm Centre, Upper Stowe, Nr Weedon, Northants NN7 4SH
Tel: 01327 349911
www.thebarnrestaurant.net

125 **Bluebells Tea Rooms**
Lock 39, Startops End, Marsworth, Tring, Herts HP23 4LJ
Tel: 01442 891708

126 **Butlers Pantry**
10 High Street, Middleton Cheney, Northants OX17 2PB
Tel: 01295 711444

127 **The Buttery**
Castle Ashby Rural Shopping Yard, Castle Ashby, Northants NN7 1LF
Tel: 01604 696728
www.thebutteryrestaurant.co.uk

128 **Canons Ashby Stables Tea Room**
Daventry, Northants NN11 3SD
Tel: 01327 860044
www.nationaltrust.org

129 **The Courtyard Tea Room**
Claydon House, Middle Claydon, Bucks MK18 2EX
Tel: 01296 730004

130 **Danesfield House**
Henley Road, Marlow-on-Thames, Bucks SL7 2EY
Tel: 01628 891010
www.danesfieldhouse.co.uk

131 **Darlingtons Tea Room**
Heart of the Shires Shopping Village, A5 Watling St, Nr Weedon NN7 4LB
Tel: 01327 342284

132 **Delapre Abbey Tea Room**
Delapre Abbey, London Road, Northampton, Northants NN4 8AW
Tel: 01604 708675
www.delapreabbey.org

133 **Dreams Coffee Shop**
59 St Giles Street, Northampton, Northants NN1 1JF
Tel: 01604 636368

134 **Ferny Hill Farm**
Ferny Hill, Hadley Wood, Nr Barnet, Herts EN4 0PZ
Tel: 020 8449 3527
www.fernyhillfarm.com

135 **Flitwick Manor**
Church Road, Flitwick, Beds MK45 1AE
Tel: 01525 712242

136 **Halsey's Tea Room**
10-11 Market Place, Hitchin, Herts SG5 1DR
Tel: 01462 432023

137 **The Hayloft Tea Room**
Boycott Farm Shop, Welsh Lane, Stowe, Bucks MK18 5DJ
Tel: 01280 821286
www.boycottfarm.co.uk

138 **The Inn at Woburn**
George Street, Woburn, Beds MK17 9PX
Tel: 01525 290441
www.theinnatwoburn.com

139 **Inn On The Park**
Verulamium Park, St. Michaels Street, St Albans, Herts AL3 4SN
Tel: 01727 838246

140 **Jenny Wrens Tea Room**
23 Market Square, Winslow, Bucks MK18 3AB
Tel: 01296 715499

141 **Kelmarsh Hall Tea Room**
Kelmarsh, Northants NN6 9LY
Tel: 01604 686543
www.kelmarsh.com

142 **Limes Farm Tea Room**
Main Road, Farthinghoe, Northants NN13 5PB
Tel: 01295 712490
www.limesfarm.com

143 **Luton Hoo**
The Mansion House, Luton, Beds LU1 3TQ
Tel: 01582 734437
www.lutonhoo.co.uk

144 **The Manor Buttery**
Sulgrave Manor, Manor Road, Sulgrave, Northants OX17 2SD
Tel: 01295 760205
www.sulgravemanor.org.uk

145 **The Mansion House**
Old Warden Park, Biggleswade, Beds SG18 9DX
Tel: 01767 626200
www.themansionhouse.org

146 **Mrs Dollys**
34 High Street, Newport Pagnell, Bucks MK16 8AR
Tel: 07432 848227

147 **The Old Tea House**
7 Windsor End, Beaconsfield, Bucks HP9 2JJ
Tel: 01494 676273

148 **Plantation Café**
Bell Plantation, Watling Street, Towcester, Northants NN12 6GX
www.bellplantation.co.uk

149 **The Rose Garden Tea Rooms**
Priory House, 33 High Street South, Dunstable, Beds LU6 3RZ
Tel: 01582 890279

150 **Seasons Cafe Deli**
6 Market Square, Amersham, Bucks HP7 0DQ
Tel: 01494 727807

151 **Sophies Tea Room at Hayden's Restaurant**
The Olde Watermill, Barton Mill Lane, Barton Le Clay, Beds MK45 4RF
Tel: 01582 882672
www.haydensrestaurant.com/sophies-tea-room

152 **Swanbourne Tea Rooms**
26-28 Winslow Road, Swanbourne, Bucks MK17 0SW
Tel: 01296 720516

153 **Teapots**
31 High Street, Olney, Bucks MK46 4AA
www.teapotsolney.co.uk

154 **Tea-Zels**
Odell Country Park, Carlton Road, Harrold, Beds MK43 7DS
Tel: 01234 721525

155 **Towcester Tea Room**
169 Watling Street, Towcester, Northants NN12 6BX
Tel: 01327 358200
www.towcestertearooms.co.uk

156 **Walled Garden Tea Room**
Castle Ashby, Northants NN7 1LQ
Tel: 01604 695200
www.castleashbygardens.co.uk

157 **Westmill Tea Room**
Westmill Village Green, Nr Buntingford, Herts SG9 9LG
Tel: 01763 274236
www.westmilltearoom.co.uk

158 **Woodlands Manor**
Green Lane, Clapham, Beds MK41 6EP
Tel: 01234 363281
www.woodlandsmanorhotel.co.uk

THE FOODIE AWARD WINNERS FOR 2012 ARE . . .

These restaurants have been voted the best in each of the four counties by our readers again this year. Thank you for all your nominations and congratulations to Mr Francis from Northampton who had his name drawn as the winner of our 2012 prize draw.

The Crooked Billet

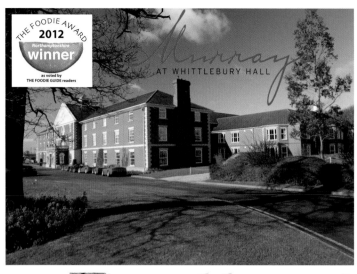

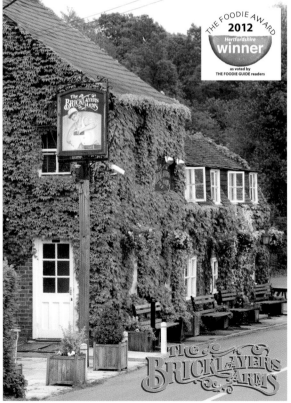

fine food & wine

All cakes made to order

fine food and wine

www.gardnerscakery.co.uk

8b Church Street, Market Harborough LE16 7AA

Telephone: 01858 468042

Email: info@gardnerscakery.co.uk

www.gardnersbakery.co.uk

85 Harborough Road, Kingsthorpe, Northampton NN2 7SL

Telephone: 01604 458555

Email: info@gardnersbakery.co.uk

fine food and wine

Beckworth Emporium is a contemporary plant centre housing a Food Hall, Produce Market, Garden Nursery and Restaurant which, since its opening in April 2009, has attracted thousands of visitors who have branded it a "truly unique shopping experience."

The Food Hall and Deli is home to Hambleton Farms – a family-run traditional farmers, butchers and game dealers supplying high-quality traditional fresh meat, game, home-made pork pies and speciality pies, home-cooked meats, hand-made sausages, haslets and much more.

A large range of high-quality ready meals and shortcrust pastry pies are also available alongside a wide selection of international, national and local cheese. Fresh bread is baked daily on site.

We've divided our Restaurant into three atmospheric areas, each individually designed including table-service offering a wide choice of delicious wholesome food using Beckworth ingredients. The stunning garden atrium is ideal for enjoying coffee, lunch and afternoon teas surrounded by our favourite colourful plants, or if the sun is shining, visitors can sit outside in the garden.

The Produce Market provides an endless selection of delicious fruit and vegetables. This fabulous display is sold alongside a range of groceries and plants.

We work hard for you to select the best of seasonal produce – offering real taste and value for money. As you pass through, you will find a selection of grocery stalls – teas and coffees, pastas and rices, cakes and biscuits, crisps and snacks and even beers and wines.

We pride ourselves on offering top-quality local produce, when possible, from suppliers who have a focus on great taste and a passion for good food.

Wander into our Garden Nursery and you'll discover a stunning array of colourful, seasonal plants, garden essentials and our container collection.

The majority of plants available are grown in our nursery enabling us to offer an adventurous range of top-quality bedding plants at very competitive prices.

These plants can be used to create a fantastic selection of beautiful hanging baskets and planted containers, brilliant for brightening up any patio and they make wonderful gifts. And if you're a novice, our expert grower Peter Taylor and the team are on hand to offer specialist tips and advice.

We look forward to welcoming you to Beckworth Emporium soon.

Opening times:	Restaurant:	
Mon-Sat 8.00 am - 6.00 pm	**Mon-Sat** 8.00 am - 5.00 pm	
Sun 11.00 am - 5.00 pm	**Sun** 9.00 am - 5.00 pm	

beckworth
emporium
FINE PRODUCE | GARDEN NURSERY | RESTAURANT

Glebe Road
Mears Ashby
Northamptonshire
NN6 0DL
Tel: 01604 812371
Email: enquiries@beckworthemporium.co.uk
www.beckworthemporium.co.uk

WINNER
NORTHAMPTONSHIRE
**FOOD
& DRINK
AWARDS
2011/12**
RESTAURANT
OF THE YEAR

fine food and wine

the larder

The Old Farmyard
Castle Ashby
Northamptonshire NN7 1LF
Tel: 01604 696742
Email: info@thelarderuk.co.uk
www.thelarderuk.co.uk

The Larder is a Gourmet Delicatessen based in the beautiful setting of Castle Ashby Rural Shopping Yard in Northamptonshire.

Specialising in:

- Local produce
- Hampers
- Outside Catering
- Wine and Spirit Sets
- Cheese Subscriptions
- Cookware
- Extensive and well established cheese counter
- Award winning pies, salamis and scotch eggs
- Patisserie
- Handmade individual chocolates
- Gluten free and free from produce

The Larder Catering The Larder offers a truly bespoke catering service, tailored to the exact needs of each individual client. By using the freshest of high quality and where possible, local ingredients, we will ensure that your expectations are surpassed. From pre-dinner canapes to original and classic main dishes, handmade desserts from our patisserie and delightful cheese boards, we can cater for your entire event. As well as fine dining, we also offer hot and cold buffets, corporate lunches and everything in between!

Our service also enables us to provide you with food that can be delivered prepared, but un-cooked - so you can pop it all in the oven when it suits you best. We can even collect your own oven dishes and platters and prepare the food for you in them - just in case you need a little hand in the kitchen!

Should you require someone to serve all the food, our chef will happily cook and serve the food at your home or event location and we can also provide a waitressing service.

Whatever the size of your event, please do not hesitate to contact us for a quote and sample menu based on your requirements.

Opening times:
Tue-Sat 10.00 am - 5.00 pm
Sundays and Bank Holidays 11.00 am - 5.00 pm

fine food and wine

Cheese Subscriptions Choose from any of the options listed on our website, whatever suits your budget, and your chosen recipient will receive a parcel of three or four carefully chosen and seasonal artisan cheeses, along with luxury cheese biscuits and tasting notes for each cheese.

A gift certificate will be despatched upon purchase and will contain full details of the gift along with all of our contact details so changes can be made to the regular delivery date to allow for any holiday periods.

For that extra bit of luxury, why not add a bottle or two of wine, designed to complement the cheeses, all from just an extra £8 per delivery.

Hampers Whether for corporate clients or a gift for family and friends, the Larder Delicatessen offers both exquisite bespoke hampers and also a whole range of devised hampers that we are sure will delight! Choose from our wide range of unique quality products, including local beers and ales, fine wines, oils and spices, preserves and chutneys, hand-made chocolates, traditional Christmas foods and luxury treats. Whether it's a Birthday, Anniversary, Christmas, or any other occasion deserving of a gift – our cheese subscriptions, bespoke hampers and cookware are sure to impress!

Starting from only £15 our hampers suit all budgets and come beautifully gift wrapped at no extra cost. Nationwide delivery service.

Products in-store We are proud of our wide range of British and European cheeses, hams, cured meats and salami, pate, award winning scotch eggs, award winning pies, chutneys and preserves!

Our high class patisserie is very much admired by all of our customers as are our fresh bread and cakes baked in store at the Larder, our 'Cook' premium home cooked prepared meals, an exclusive wine selection along with internationally acclaimed spirits, an olive, vinegar and oil station which consists of award winning olives and a range of premium flavoured oils and vinegars – available on tap – and a cookware section that is prefect for your own use or an inspiring gift!

Hand Made Chocolates We have recently introduced a chocolate counter which boasts over 30 individual hand-made chocolates: tremendously popular with everyone that comes in to the shop!

Browns of Stagsden
FARM SHOP

Manor Farm
High Street
Stagsden
Bedford
MK43 8SQ
Tel: 01234 822330
Email: info@brownsofstagsden.co.uk
www.brownsofstagsden.co.uk

The Brown family has farmed in and around Bedfordshire for many years, and three generations are now involved in the business. The family has always taken great pride in growing crops and rearing cattle, pigs and turkeys, so they decided to open a shop at Manor Farm, in the beautiful village of Stagsden.

Christmas Turkeys have been sold from the farm since 1949. The shop opened in 2005 and with an extension in 2008 offers a wide range of locally grown produce to an ever increasing customer base.

Traditional breeds of cattle, pigs and turkeys are reared for the shop using home-grown grain where possible, whilst lambs and free range chickens are reared locally. The beef is hung for at least three weeks for maximum tenderness and flavour.

Game is also available when in season. All sausages, burgers and ready meals are prepared on site and you will also be able to buy local vegetables, cheeses, hams, organic flour, fresh bread, gluten-free cakes, free range eggs, local milk, ice-creams and tempting accompaniments. Why not also come and try our home cured bacon and charcuterie or our home cured turkey bacon?

In the run up to Christmas - a very busy time of the year for Browns - you will be able to pre-order your home-reared turkey and any other meats, or choose from our wide range of hampers which make for excellent presents.

So if you are looking for something different and enjoy good quality produce, please pay the shop a visit, where our helpful staff will offer you a warm welcome. Why not stop and enjoy a coffee whilst you shop with us?

Opening times:
Tue-Thur 9.00 am - 5.00 pm
Fri 9.00 am - 6.00 pm (Fresh Fish available 9.00 am - 3.00 pm)
Sat 9.00 am - 4.00 pm (Fresh Fish available 9.00 am - 3.00 pm)

Follow us on Facebook and Twitter

Love Food. Love Frosts.

At Frosts we believe in providing good quality, affordable fresh food, for good living. We source only the finest ingredients and hand select all of our products to compliment seasonal changes.

We stock an extensive range of products including locally sourced fresh fruit and vegetables, hand made cakes and pies and a wide range of packaged produce from baked beans and cereals to artisan chutneys. Our fully stocked delicatessen counter offers delicious cheeses, pâtés and olives which taste fantastic alongside our bread which is baked freshly every morning. Whether you are looking for that extra treat for a dinner party or simply need a pint of milk, Frosts Food Hall offers great value convenience shopping.

Open seven days a week we have created a shopping experience that will meet all of your culinary requirements.

Woburn Country Foods Butchers Counter

Woburn Country Foods butchers counter, located in Frosts Food Hall is fully staffed and completely stocked with top quality local meats from the surrounding counties. They are committed to sourcing only the best meats from Bedfordshire and Buckinghamshire, giving customer's peace of mind that only local produce is stocked…and all at Farmers Market prices.

Frosts Garden Centre at Woburn Sands, Newport Road, Woburn Sands, Milton Keynes, MK17 8UE **Tel:** 01908 583511

www.frostsgroup.com

SUMMERHILL FARM SHOP

Cople Road, Cardington, Bedfordshire MK44 3SH
Tel: 01234 831222
Email: sales@summerhillfarmshop.co.uk
www.summerhillfarmshop.co.uk

Set in the picturesque village of Cardington, home of the famous Cardington airship hangars, Summerhill Farm Shop takes great pride in sourcing the very best in local and seasonal produce. The shop is now under the management of Sally Carmichael and new Head Butcher James Fraser.

We are part of the Southill Estate which raises entirely grass-fed British White cattle for sale exclusively through the farm shop. The beef is hung for the full, traditional 28 days, allowing it to mature on the bone for that unique flavour and tenderness that can only be achieved by the maturing process. Cuts and joints can be ordered in advance and viewed over time whilst they are maturing. Such is the demand for our White beef that we do need to source some additional local beef but always ensure that it is farmed ethically and in line with our own very high standards of husbandry. Our lamb and freerange chicken are sourced from farms within Cardington village and the pork is from nearby St Neots. All of our meat is expertly butchered on site to the customers' exact requirements but, in addition to the more traditional cuts, handmade sausages and burgers, there is an extensive range of our own gourmet and "ready to cook" lines such as chicken filo pastries, stir fries, marinated meats and the Summerhill Traditional Pork Sausage, winner of Bedford's Best Sausage (Taste Real Food – Bedford). And of course we have local turkeys for Christmas!

The Southill Estate is also home to Warden Abbey Vineyard, Bedfordshire's only working vineyard, and their range of English wine including the award-winning Warden Abbot Sparkling is available in the farm shop along with a bespoke selection of South African and new world wines sourced by Charles Whitbread, owner of the Estate. We also stock a wide range of English fruit and country wines and several locally produced beers, ales and ciders.

Our deli counter has a great range of carefully selected artisan and award-winning cheeses, mainly from within the UK, and cold meats including the delicious Bedfordshire Black Ham, Suffolk salami and chorizo, olives and antipasti, pies, quiches and patés. The cheese and meat are complemented by a very good choice of savoury biscuits and chutneys and pickles all sourced as locally as possible. Other local produce includes eggs which are all free-range from the same farm in Cardington as our chickens, cakes, fruit pies and bread produced by local bakers and delivered daily. In addition, we work very closely with local farmers' co-operatives and distributors to source local fruit and vegetables, grown naturally and in season.

Opening times:
Mon-Fri 9.00 am - 6.00 pm
Sat 8.00 am - 5.00 pm
Sun 10.00 am - 4.00 pm

We can be found just three miles south east of Bedford – exit from the A421 at the Sandy A603 junction and follow the signs to Summerhill Farm Shop and Cardington from the roundabout.

BOYCOTT FARM SHOP

Welsh Lane, Stowe, Bucks MK18 5DJ
Tel: 01280 821286
Email: shop@boycottfarm.co.uk
PLEASE VISIT OUR WEBSITE FOR MORE INFORMATION AND OUR LATEST NEWS AND OFFERS
www.boycottfarm.co.uk

Boycott farm shop is situated in the middle of beautiful North Buckinghamshire countryside, close to the National Trust Estate at Stowe. Our wonderful 17c barn was sensitively restored and converted in 2008, and is now home to our popular Farm Shop and The Hayloft Restaurant and Tearoom.

As a working farm we rear and produce premium quality Aberdeen Angus Beef and Traditional Breed Pork along with our fresh, free-range eggs. Using our own and local produce, we prepare a wonderful selection of homemade cakes, quiches and an extensive range of wholesome ready meals which we sell in our Farm Shop and serve in The Hayloft. Alongside our own produce our shop is well stocked with bread, milk, vegetables and much more. We also offer a range of foods for meetings, parties or special gatherings from our new Catering Selection.

Described as an "oasis" in the Buckinghamshire countryside, The Hayloft Restaurant and Tearoom serves delicious homemade food, freshly made to order. From Monday to Saturday we offer Full English Breakfast, Lunch and Afternoon Tea. On Sundays, we serve Roast Sunday Lunch with hand carved meat, homemade Yorkshire puddings, roast potatoes and gravy.

We believe in good, old fashioned customer service and are very proud of our friendly, helpful staff. You will always receive a warm welcome at Boycott Farm.

Opening times:
SHOP:
Mon-Sat 8.00 am - 6.00 pm
Sun 10.00 am - 4.00 pm

BUTCHERY:
Mon-Sat 8.00 am - 5.00 pm
Sun 10.00 am - 4.00 pm

THE HAYLOFT:
Mon-Fri 9.00 am - 5.00 pm
Sat 8.30 am - 5.00 pm
Sun 10.00 am - 4.00 pm

fine food and wine

DELICATESSEN ESTRELLA

2A High Street
Winslow
Buckinghamshire
MK18 3HF
Tel: 01296 712466
www.delicatessenestrella.co.uk

Located in the heart of the pretty market town in Winslow, right opposite the Market Square, Delicatessen Estrella specialises in providing the best food and ingredients available to bring you the flavours of the Mediterranean. Helen and John Knight have a passion for all food, especially that of Spain and North Africa and always stock an excellent range of unusual Spanish products, including charcuterie and cheeses.

Throughout the shop the emphasis is always on food of the highest quality, which they source from the best suppliers in their fields, including cheeses from Neal's Yard Dairy and Spanish meats from Brindisa. Helen's home cooking is a huge hit with customers. From home baked pasties, pies, quiches and cakes through to a seasonally changing selection of delicious homemade, ready prepared, frozen bistro meals and accompaniments, all using local meat and produce. In summer, fresh salads are available and in the colder months, seasonal soups to take home. An excellent range of ethically produced coffees are ground to order and fresh artisan bread is available several days a week.

Estrella opens every Friday night until 7pm to make it easy for busy workers to pick up a one stop meal. This might range from a tapas selection or an antipasto plate to a cheese board, cake or pudding. Complement your food with their selection of great wines and sherries, or try a few bottles from a popular range of locally brewed real ales.

So if you love good food and are looking for the best products and ingredients for yourself, or a food or drink related gift like their popular Christmas baskets and hampers made to order, make sure you visit Delicatessen Estrella.

Opening times:
Mon-Thur 10:00 – 17:30
Fri 10:00 – 19:00
Sat 09:30 – 17:00
Sun Farmers Market Sundays (1st Sunday of each month) and December 10:00 – 14:00

Dobbies Garden World
Belvedere Lane
Watling Street
Fenny Stratford
Milton Keynes MK17 9JH
Tel: 01908 364890
Fax: 01908 364891
Email: miltonkeynes@dobbies.com
www.dobbies.com

Dobbies
GARDEN CENTRES

Opening times:
Mon 9.00 am - 6.00 pm
Tue 9.30 am - 6.00 pm
Wed-Fri 9.00 am - 6.00 pm
Sat-Sun 9.00 am - 6.00 pm
Open till 8pm in peak seasons

Fill your larder…

Treat yourself to a harvest of fresh produce at Dobbies Farm Foodhall.

Throughout the seasons as nature slowly opens her larder we offer an abundance of fresh fruit and vegetables.

Enjoy nature's harvest of plenty and fill your own larder by visiting the **Farm Foodhall at Dobbies Garden World Milton Keynes** – a destination for food lovers looking for the best of locally and internationally sourced produce.

Freshly made in store …

Continuing the reputation for expertise that Dobbies established in 1865, the Foodhall's bakers produce quality goods, daily, in store.

Treat yourself to delicious cakes, pies and artisan breads baked freshly on the premises.

Seasonal produce, sourced locally…

By partnering with nearby fruit and vegetable growers, wherever possible, Dobbies aims to bring you the best in field, in store, just hours after each new harvest.

Choose from field-fresh potatoes, leeks, turnips, radishes and onions. Or pick from locally-grown fruits including raspberries, blueberries, blackberries, cranberries and currants.

Local and continental tastes …

Visit the Farm Foodhall's delicatessen and savour hand-made farmhouse cheeses crafted just a few miles from store or brie, mozzarella and other continental cheese board favourites.

Try cured meats, stuffed olives and artisan cheeses with Foodhall's free sampling service. Choose to complement your choice with quality beers, liqueurs, spirits and fine wines.

Visit the **Farm Foodhall at Dobbies Milton Keynes** and treat yourself to a harvest of quality produce. **Dobbies Garden World Milton Keynes, Belvedere Lane, Watling Street, Fenny Stratford, Milton Keynes, MK17 9JH.**

fine food and wine

1 Odells Yard
High Street
Stony Stratford
Milton Keynes MK11 1AQ
Tel: 01908 568000

Opening times:
Mon-Sat 9:00 – 17:30

Following on from the success of Cameron's Brasserie, the talented team and Chef Owner Dan Cameron have opened Cameron's Delicatessen and Coffee House in the beautiful setting of Odell's Yard, Stony Stratford.

The Cameron's ethos stays true with the emphasis on ingredients and produce of the highest quality. The delicatessen stocks all you might expect and more, with the range including locally sourced, speciality and homemade produce, from pies to fresh vegetables.

One of the highlights is the freshly baked bread, available on a daily basis, made by skilled Chefs. Why not pick up a loaf at lunchtime and sample the exciting lunch menu offering gourmet sandwiches and salads at the same time?

Ever wondered what to do with that speciality ingredient? Just ask! The team will be only too pleased to answer any questions you might have, share their expert advice and provide recipe suggestions. Still struggling to find what you're looking for? Sometimes a dish requires a certain ingredient that you just can't get your hands on anywhere. Ask about the 'Order In' service as the likelihood is they will be able to source it for you, whatever it may be; fresh fish or a spice.

So if you're fed up with supermarkets and appreciate good food, make sure you visit Cameron's Delicatessen and Coffee House soon.

BEST BUTCHERS Ltd

Unit 5
Lower Rectory Farm
Great Brickhill
Milton Keynes
MK17 9AF
Tel: 01908 375275
Email: shop@thebestbutchers.co.uk
www.thebestbutchers.co.uk

Quality, variety and a commitment to personal service sum up Simon Boddy's "Best Butchers Ltd".

Situated on a working organic farm Best Butchers is owned and run by Simon Boddy. Since 1994 Simon has been specialising in supplying locally sourced meat and is justly proud to supply most of the best restaurants in the area.

Besides joints and fine cuts of beef, lamb, pork and poultry this absolutely spotless shop is renowned for its fine pork, beef and lamb sausages all prepared on the premises along with bacon, dry-cured and slowly smoked over beech.

Recently Simon has added a maturation room for salamis and air dried meats. The process involves patience and products are only made available when absolutely ready. Having spent a number of years developing, the team are now actively encouraging customers to compare their product against European counterparts – I think they will be pleasantly surprised. Brickhill ham is Simon's own adaption of Parma ham.

Acclaimed by Rose Prince of the Daily Telegraph that the air-dried coppa was the best air-dried meat she had tasted in Britain and the Sunday Observer rated them as "Best Deli".

Opening times:
Mon-Tue Closed
Wed 8.00 am - 12.00 pm
Thur-Fri 8.00 am - 5.00 pm
Sat 8.00 am - 2.00 pm
Sun Closed

fine food and wine

Aubergine Fine Food & Wines

73 High Street
Woburn Sands
Bucks MK17 8QY
Tel: 01908 582020
Email: auberginedeli@btconnect.com

Aubergine Fine Foods is an independent, family-owned delicatessen and wine merchant in Woburn Sands, established by local residents Jill and John Goulding. Run by food lovers for food lovers, Aubergine strives to offer international speciality foods alongside the finest locally-sourced produce. John is also happy to share his expert advice to help find a perfect wine match for any food.

The ever expanding range includes British and continental cheeses, salamis and chorizos, pastas, cooking sauces, preserves, chocolates, breads and biscuits, plus all the kitchen cupboard essentials.

Wherever possible Aubergine sources foods from local, small-scale producers, including free-range eggs from Lidlington; bacon, sausages and hams from their butcher's own farm in Bedfordshire; bread from Ampthill; plus

Opening times:
Mon-Fri 8.00 am - 5.00 pm
Sat 9.00 am - 4.00 pm

honey, vegetables and delicious home-made cakes from Woburn Sands itself.

In addition, there is an increasing range of 'free from' foods for people with special dietary requirements, including gluten-free pastas, cereals and biscuits. Aubergine is also an ethical and environmentally responsible business. Many products are fairly traded, offering producers in the developing world a better deal, and all the shop's own packaging is bio-degradable, recyclable, or from a sustainable source.

Latest developments include a new lunch menu offering pasta dishes, home-made savoury tartlets, filled ciabatta rolls and gourmet salads, plus great coffee and fresh fruit smoothies. A business and event menu is also available with free local delivery. And for those of you looking for something a bit different for your special event or even wedding, we can provide a portable wood fired pizza oven with your personal pizza chef.

Whatever your culinary tastes, if you're passionate about food and looking for an alternative to the supermarket experience, pay a visit to Aubergine - your local, independent fine food store.

Riverford
organic farms

stock up your kitchen & cut down on shopping trips

Riverford delivers award-winning organic food fresh from Sacrewell Farm straight to your door. There's nothing Riverford doesn't know about fruit and veg (they've been growing it for nearly 25 years) but the farm has plenty more to offer. Choose from a range of weekly organic essentials like eggs, milk, meat, juice and cereal, and even wine, chocolate, pasta and olive oil. Delivery is free and you don't need to be at home.

get inspired & cook seasonally

You'll want to make the most of all that fresh seasonal food and Riverford makes it easy. With each delivery your local vegman (or lady) will

bring up to eight new recipes to inspire you to feed your family better. Forget boring boiled vegetables: swap them for sweet and tasty honey-glazed carrots or grilled courgettes and tomatoes with basil dressing. Riverford's website is bursting with

even more recipes. And if you ever run out of ideas, just call the team at the farm for help.

easy to order

Ordering is easy and flexible. Riverford delivers weekly, fortnightly or whenever suits and you can stop and start deliveries as often as you like. Make up your own order from the full range or try a vegbox from just £9.85 with free delivery.

www.riverford.co.uk/sacrewell
01780 789700

fine food and wine

Smiths Farm Shop

Chapel Brampton Shop Tel: 01604 843206
Brampton Lane, Chapel Brampton, Northampton, Northants NN6 8AA
Mon-Sat 9.00am - 5.30pm Sun 10.00am - 1.00pm
Email: smithsfarmshop@btinternet.com **www.smithsfarmshop.co.uk**

Now at three convenient locations within Northamptonshire Smith's Farm Shop is a retailer of quality fresh farm foods and fine country produce. Selling fresh seasonal fruit and vegetables from British growers, including produce grown on their own farm situated behind the shop at Chapel Brampton. Aiming to source from producers most local ensures products arrive on the shelves in near-perfect condition, bursting with flavour and with the highest nutritional value. Regular customers say they come back time and again because Smith's produce can't be beaten for freshness and flavour, all at prices that compare well against larger U.K. food retailers.

Outside each shop you will find garden and pet supplies, plants and solid fuels. Inside the shops you will be greeted by a spacious layout for all the main food categories such as fruit and vegetables, jams and preserves, frozen foods, delicatessen, dairy products, eggs, cakes and pastries, bakery and meat. The quiet, relaxed atmosphere will help make your shopping trip more of a pleasurable experience, and less of a chore. They also stock ranges of non-food products, mainly for the home, garden and pets along with a small selection of greeting cards.

Towcester Shop Tel: 01327 358358
Bell Plantation, Watling Street, Towcester, Northants NN12 6GX
Mon-Sun 10.00am - 4.30pm

A great shopping experience awaits you at Smith's Farm Shop. For your convenience, they have a large car park right outside the shop entrances. Friendly members of staff are always ready to help carry your purchases to the car. They provide a relaxed and enjoyable shopping experience and at the Chapel Brampton site, you will find several other attractions to add a bit of fun and interest to your shopping trip!

Great Billing Shop Tel: 01604 412111
Billing Garden Village, The Causeway, Great Billing, Northants NN3 9EX
Mon-Sun 10.00am - 4.30pm

fine food and wine

Stony Wine Emporium

2 Odell's Yard
Stony Stratford
Milton Keynes
Buckinghamshire
MK11 1AQ
Tel: 01908 267373
Email: info@stonywineemporium.co.uk
www.stonywineemporium.co.uk

The Stony Wine Emporium opened in October 2009 and is the creation of Simon & Caroline Stagnell. Simon has enjoyed over 20 years in the wine trade, representing a vast range of wineries, estates and icon producers. His passion, knowledge and experience gained over these years provided the inspiration to open a new wine shop concept situated in the charming historic market town of Stony Stratford in north Buckinghamshire.

All the wines have been tasted, carefully selected and represent the best available from their domaine. There are always over 250 wines available on the shelves, which are constantly changing as they discover new and exciting vineyards and producers.

They offer wine purchasing at all levels, from everyday drinking to premium estate wines. There is always an opportunity to taste when you visit along with access to good advice and guidance.

Private tastings can be arranged for groups of friends, work colleagues and corporate clients, either at the shop or your choice of local venue, there are a large range of subjects on offer, which are aimed to be informative and fun.

The Wine Café is open daily serving lunches from 12.00 pm onwards offering some delicious anti pasti, cheese & meat platters to share, along with some tasty salads and light lunches. Dining is casual with a good selection of wines available by the glass and all the wines can be picked off the shelf for just a £5 supplement.

Opening times:
Sun/Mon Closed
Tue-Sat Owing to seasonal differences please check website for details.

fine food and wine

fine food and wine

The Bull Pen
— in the evening —

NEW for 2012... by day the Bull Pen is a delightful tearoom and by night it has been transformed into an exquisite fine dining experience where you will find a warm and inviting ambience amid natural oak, and timber beams.

The Bull Pen in the evening delivers a unique blend of elegant sophistication with excellent service and an exceptional modern British menu featuring our own home reared beef and a full range of engaging wines.

The Bull Pen, embraces the unassuming natural beauty of the 220 acre farm and rural shopping village on which it resides, whilst only 16 miles from Marble Arch, it's *the* new place to eat in Radlett.

Contact us now to book your table
01923 857505 | info@thebullpenrestaurant.co.uk
www.thebullpenrestaurant.co.uk

fine food and wine

Learn, Make and Taste Real Food Now

Taste Real Food brings together people from all walks
of life to experience local seasonal produce through
supporting our farmers, artisan producers and local outlets
that champion Real Food. Outreaching to the youth
and breaking down cultural barriers with an emphasis
on equality and mental wellbeing. We are proud to have
a new base at 123 Create, Midland Road, Bedford
working in partnership with Bedford Create Arts
we will deliver Food, Music and Art to the community
raising self esteem and creating fun and enjoyment for all

To find out more and join us at our events contact
tasterealfoodbedford@ntlworld.com
or find us on facebook - Taste Real Food

63 High Street
Newport Pagnell
MK16 8AT
Tel: 01908 410501
Email: eat@pic-nics.co.uk
www.pic-nics.co.uk
Facebook: www.facebook.com/PicNicsNewportPagnell
Twitter: @pic_nics

Opening times:
Mon-Fri 8.00 am - 5.00 pm
Sat 9.00 am - 5.00 pm
Sun Closed

PicNic's arrived on the High Street of Newport Pagnell in July 2012 following an extensive refurbishment of long-standing premises. Since then, PicNic's has been winning over the hearts and stomachs of all those stopping to sample its delights.

It's not just those stopping by who've been impressed by PicNic's. Catering for external events has also proved immediately successful with local businesses quick to provide tremendous feedback.

PicNic's makes its own quiche, stews, soups, cakes and sandwiches with bread being provided by a local artisan producer. No wonder people have described it as "out of this world!" Just as well you can buy a whole loaf to take home.

Whether it's enjoying the zip provided by some of the best Union coffee or savouring the velvety hot chocolate from Marimba, literally made with a whole bar of chocolate! PicNic's has the perfect drink for the occasion. Or perhaps you'd prefer a fresh fruit smoothie on a Summer's day; PicNic's has that covered, too.

PicNic's also provides a full deli-range including delicious meats, cheeses, olives, oils and vinegars, all of which can be sampled before buying. And if you're looking for a tasty treat for Christmas, a birthday, any special occasion, or even just because, PicNic's offers personalised hampers.

Inspired by some of the top delis around the country, and committed to sustainability, Nicola O'Brien, PicNic's owner and a self-confessed foodie, has brought the very best mix of locally sourced produce and flavours from further afield to the people of Buckinghamshire.

fine food and wine

FARMERS MARKETS

Whilst every effort has been made compiling this list, we cannot accept responsibility when dates/times/places are changed.

Bedfordshire

Ampthill	The Prince of Wales pub car park	Last Saturday every month (except December)	9.00am - 1.00pm
Bedford	Harpur Square	2nd & 4th Thursday every month	9.00am - 2.00pm
Biggleswade	Market Square	3rd Wednesday every month	9.00am - 2.00pm
Cranfield	The Cross Keys pub	2nd Sunday every month	9.00am - 1.00pm
Dunstable Downs	Chiltern Gateway Centre	1st Sunday every month (except January)	10.00am - 2.00pm
Leighton Buzzard	High Street	3rd Saturday every month	9.00am - 2.00pm
Milton Ernest	Garden Centre Country Food Fayre	3rd Saturday every month	10.00am - 3.00pm
Sandy	Sandy Car Park	1st Saturday every month (except January)	9.00am - 1.00pm
Shefford	High Street	2nd Saturday every month	9.00am - 1.00pm
Woburn	The Pitching's, Woburn	3rd Sunday every month	11.00am - 3.00pm

Buckinghamshire

Aylesbury	Old Market Square	4th Tuesday every month	9.00am - 2.00pm
Beaconsfield	Windsor End, The Old Town	4th Saturday every month	9.00am - 12.30pm
Buckingham	Old Cattle Pens, High Street	1st Tuesday every month	7.30am - 1.00pm
Little Chalfont	Village Hall car park, Cokes Lane	2nd Saturday every month	9.00am - 1.00pm
Marlow	Dean Street car park	Every Sunday	10.00am - 1.00pm
Newport Pagnell	Market Hill, High Street	3rd Friday every month	9.00am - 2.00pm
Olney	Market Place	1st Sunday every month	10.00am - 2.00pm
Prestwood	Hildreths Garden Centre, Wycombe Rd.	Every Friday	8.00am - 1.00pm
Princes Risborough	High Street	3rd Thursday every month	8.30am - 1.30pm
Stony Stratford	Market Square	Last Friday every month	8.30am - 1.30pm
Wendover	Off High Street	3rd Saturday every month	10.00am - 1.00pm
Winslow	Market Square	First Sunday every month	11.00am - 2.00pm
Wolverton	Market Halls car park, Town Hall	1st & 3rd Saturdays every month	9.00am - 1.00pm

Hertfordshire

Dane End	Dane End Memorial Hall	2nd Saturday every month	10.30am - 12.30pm
Great Amwell	Van Hage Garden Company	1st Thursday every month	9.00am - 1.00pm
Gt Hormead	Village Hall	1st Saturday every month	10.00am - 12.30pm
Harpenden	Lower High Street	4th Saturday every month	10.00am - 2.00pm
Hatfield	White Lion Square	1st Saturday every month (except January)	9.00am - 2.00pm
Hertford	Market Place	2nd Saturday every month	9.00am - 1.00pm
Hertford Heath	Village Hall	3rd Sunday every month	9.00am - 1.00pm
Hitchin	Riverside	Last Saturday every month	8.00am - 2.00pm
Hoddesdon	The Clock Tower	3rd Friday every month	9.00am - 2.00pm
Leominster	Corn Square	2nd Saturday every month	9.00am - 1.00pm
Little Hadham	Village Hall	Last Saturday every month	9.00am - 12.00pm
Royston	Town Hall	1st Friday every month	9.30am - 1.00pm
Sandon	Village Hall	3rd Saturday every month	9.30am - 12.00pm
St Albans	Town Hall	2nd Sunday every month	9.00am - 2.00pm
Tring	Market Place	Alternate Saturdays	9.00am - 12.15pm

Northamptonshire

Brackley	Market Place	3rd Saturday every month	9.00am - 1.00pm
Daventry	High Street	1st Saturday every month	8.30am - 1.30pm
Higham Ferrers	Market Square	Last Saturday every month	8.00am - 3.00pm
Kettering	Wicksteed Park	3rd Sunday every month	9.00am - 2.00pm
Northampton	Market Square	3rd Thursday every month	9.00am - 1.30pm
Oundle	Market Street	2nd Saturday every month	9.00am - 2.00pm
Towcester	Richmond Rd car park	2nd Friday every month	9.00am - 2.00pm
Wellingborough	Market Place	Last Thursday every month	9.00am - 2.00pm

farmers markets

Chef Profile

Describe your style of cooking

Traditional British with a continental modern twist. I am very precise and like to pack dishes with flavour, (my sorbet's can use a whole tray of fruit) exploring unusual marriages of tastes that really work in combination, to the mantra of only the very best will do.

Current speciality

Traditional / deconstructed / intensely flavoured / taken to the enth degree / One of my signature dishes is a favourite of regular diners and often requested – home smoked warm salmon with curry oil and garlic sauce and black pudding; oh and there is the famous 'PatPat' which has quite a following...milk marinated Goosnargh chicken liver Pate (no bitterness there!)

What do you love most about your job?

Pleasing people through the shared joy of food. It is my life and passion. I am so lucky to be doing what I enjoy and consider it my life's work.

Training and background

After training in Essex, I worked in London before moving out to the country and taking on the restoration of the Northamptonshire stone Vine House and establishing the Hotel and Restaurant more than two decades ago. Life as a Chef is a continual learning journey as I am always researching and pushing forward with my cooking, honing my skills, striving always for perfection to delight my diners.

What prompted you to become a Chef?

Being a Chef is part of my core, it was always something I wanted to do since boyhood. I've always loved food and being a chef seemed the only natural thing to do. I started in London.....met Julie, my darling wife whom diners will recognise as she works front of house whilst I am in the kitchen, and together our dream was to have our own restaurant, the rest is history.

Marcus Springett

In The Kitchen

Bubble & Squeak and Mustard Gravy

Ingredients - Serves 4

For Sausages
- 675g Steak & Kidney
- 1 Small Onion
- 1 Garlic Clove
- 1 tbsp Parsley (chopped)
- 1 Bay Leaf
- 1 tbsp Sage (chopped)
- Salt & Pepper
- 1 Egg Yolk

For Bubble & Squeak
- 115g Cooked Cabbage
- 50g Cooked Leek
- 50g Cooked Spinach
- 225g Mashed Potato
- Salt & Pepper
- Oil for pan frying

For Deep Fried Onions
- 300ml Milk
- Seasoned Flour
- Oil for deep frying
- 225g Mashed Potato
- Salt & Pepper

For Mustard Gravy
- 600ml Veal Stock
- 25g Grain Mustard
- 25g Butter (cut into pieces)
- Salt & Pepper

Method

To make the sausages: Mince all the ingredients and season. Bind together with the egg yolk. Divide the mixture into eight and roll into thick sausage shapes. Wrap each one carefully in Clingfilm and chill for about 1 hour in the fridge. Poach the wrapped sausages in simmering water for 10 minutes, then remove and dip into a bowl of cold water to refresh. Chill until required. *To prepare the onions for deep frying:* Simply slice and put into a bowl, cover with the milk and leave for about 1 hour.

1 Remove Clingfilm from the sausages and grill them on all sides for about 3 minutes until cooked. **2** Mix together the ingredients for the bubble and squeak, heat a little oil in a frying pan and fry the mixture on both sides until golden. **3** Drain the onions; dip in seasoned flour and deep fry until crispy. **4** For the gravy, bring the stock to the boil in a pan then whisk in the mustard and butter until the gravy is thick and shiny. Season to taste. *To serve:* Cut the bubble and squeak into 4 slices and place each slice in the centre of a plate. Top each slice with 2 sausages, pile the crisp onions on top, then pour a little of the mustard gravy around the outside.

Chef Profile

Describe your style of cooking
Traditional and Fresh.

Current speciality
Half a Roast Shoulder of Grafton Regis Lamb, on a Bed of Colcannon Mash with a rich Sauce of Homegrown Damson, Rosemary and Port.

Training and brackground
Two years at catering college and 30 years in the real world, now a Fellow Member of the British Institute of Innkeepers. Just been accepted as a Fellow Member of the Academy of Food and Wine Service. And a Master Craftsman with the Craft Guild of Chefs.

What do you love most about your job?
The feedback, I love pleasing people with food, overhearing a conversation at a table when they are complimenting the food is the best compliment.

What prompted you to become a Chef?
My teacher at school said everything was being taken over by computers so pick something that can`t be. I chose catering and never looked back.

Which seasonal produce do you look forward to?
Grafton Regis Lamb, we serve it as often as we can get it, Paddocks Farm in Grafton Regis have won awards for Lamb, and there is nothing else like it.

What's your favourite food combo?
I don't have a favourite, but some things work strangely together, try fresh English Strawberries cut in half and sprinkled with fresh ground pepper, amazing with cheese.

How do you like to unwind?
With a nice bottle of Rioja and friends in the sunshine, when we can get some.

What's your preferred home cooked meal?
A good wholesome stew and dumplings.

Alan Drake F.B.I.I. / F.A.F.W.S. / M.C.G.C. _____

The White Hart, Grafton Regis

In The Kitchen

Ingredients - Serves 4
- Half Shoulder of English Lamb
- Few Sprigs Fresh Rosemary
- Enough Potatoes for 4
- 4 Spring Onions (finely chopped)
- 500g Savoy Cabbage (finely sliced)
- 500g Damsons
- Knob of Butter
- 100g Brown Sugar
- 50ml Port
- Salt & Pepper

Method
1 *Day One:* Place lamb in a roasting tray, season with salt and pepper and place a couple of rosemary sprigs on top. Cover with foil and place in the oven at 180°c for 4 hrs. When it's cooked remove the foil and pour off the juices, this is better done the day before serving, allow the juices to cool, then place in a refrigerator until the fat has set on top, remove the fat and set aside for the roast potatoes. Keep the rest of the stock to make the sauce.

2 *Day Two:* Put damsons and sugar in a saucepan with a tight fitting lid and place on a low light, allow the damsons to cook down 15-20 mins, strain through a sieve and reserve for the sauce.

3 Peel and cut potatoes, put into a pan, cover with water, add a pinch of salt. When potatoes are almost cooked take out half for roasting and allow the rest to further cook for the mash. Heat the fat in a roasting tray in the oven and put in the potatoes for roasting, with a couple of sprigs of rosemary and a pinch of salt, place in the oven at 200°c/Gas 6 for 30-40 mins turning and basting them half-way through cooking.

4 Put the lamb back into the oven uncovered 200°c/Gas 6 to brown and crisp up the fat. About 20 mins for the lamb if it's hot but if you have cooked it the day before allow 30-40 mins.

5 Put the stock (fat removed) into a large saucepan, add the damson juice and port and simmer well until reduced to a nice sauce consistency, taste and add sugar/salt/pepper to taste.

6 Place the finely chopped cabbage and spring onions in a small Tupperware container with a little butter and a pinch of salt and place in the microwave for 2 mins or until the cabbage is starting to soften a little. This can be done on a low light in a pan.

7 Strain off the cooked potatoes for mash, leave the lid off for a few mins to allow the steam to escape and the potatoes to dry out a little, add the cabbage and the buttery juices, salt and pepper to taste and mash them well with a masher or use a hand whisk on slow, add more butter or a drop of cream.

8 Place the mash in the centre of a large serving dish, sit the roasted lamb in the centre on top, arrange the roast potatoes around the edge and pour a little of the sauce over the lamb, serve the rest separately. Serve with lots of fresh vegetables.

Half Slow Roasted Shoulder of Lamb with Colcannon Mash,

Paris House

Füri

Buckwheat Blini - A Summer Canapé

Chef Profile

Describe your style of cooking
Modern British, taking classical flavours and giving them a modern twist.

Current speciality
I don't really have a speciality but the dish I am the most happy with at the moment is a Kentucky Fried Veal Sweetbread with sweetcorn, wild mushrooms and BBQ sauce.

Training and brackground
I have many chefs to thank for my training over the years but the three that molded me more than the rest are Mr Conahan, Michael MacDonald and Alan Murchison. Henley College; The Vanilla Pod, Marlow; L'ortolan, Reading; respectively each place teaching me something different. I started working in pubs and really enjoyed the freedom of constantly changing dishes and ended in Michelin starred kitchens where I love working with passionate foodies and the best ingredients we can find.

What prompted you to become a Chef?
I've always loved to cook. From a very early age I would keep myself entertained in the kitchen, so it was a very natural progression from hobby to job.

Which seasonal produce do you look forward to?
Wild mushrooms, girolles and cepes particularly. Summer fruits, the peach and nectarine; Venison!

What's your favourite food combo?
Cheese and pickle.

How do you like to unwind?
Playing with my baby daughter and eating out with Claire my long suffering wife.

What's your preferred home cooked meal?
Home made pizza, fun for all the family and it tastes good.

Do you have a favourite cook book?
Oriol Balaguer, Dessert Cuisine, The French Laundry.

Phil Fanning

In The Kitchen

Ingredients

For the Blini:
- 150g Milk
- 8g Fresh Yeast
- 75g Buckwheat Flour
- 50g Plain Flour
- 1 Egg Yolk
- 150g Egg White

For the Salad:
- 1 small Beetroot (baked and finely diced)
- 1 small Granny Smith Apple (finely diced)
- 25g Aylesbury Escargots Pearls
- 1 tsp Thyme Leaves
- 1 tbsp Vinaigrette
- Maldon Sea Salt to taste

Method

1. Mix all the Blini ingredients together in a bowl with a whisk and leave covered in the fridge overnight.
2. Spoon small dots of the batter into a medium hot frying pan with a tiny bit of oil and cook the Blini until it is golden on both sides.
3. Mix all the salad ingredients together then spoon a generous helping onto a Blini, best enjoyed with a glass of bubbles or iced Vodka.

behind the scenes

Chef Profile

Describe your style of cooking
French Traditional.

Current speciality
Grilled meats but my strongest is fish.

Training and brackground
I have twenty years experience; apprentice from 1989 to 1992, worked in the kitchen in the army for a year, then worked in Switzerland, Luxembourg, USA in 5 Star restaurant and then Sous Chef in Michelin Star La Toque Blanch, then became an Executive Chef in the UK.

What do you love most about your job?
I love everything about my job but love it even more when I have a special occasion, special events where I can prepare different dishes that require more technical work and where I can use my creativity.

What prompted you to become a Chef?
As an apprentice I wanted to become a Pastry Chef but my life took a different path when I worked with Master Chef Lebrun Bernard, I knew then that my passion had changed.

What's your favourite food combo?
Terrine's de campagne, gherkins, homemade chutney, hams, salamis and French Baguette with a nice glass of Bordeaux.

How do you like to unwind?
Spending good quality time with my family, watching sports and playing Petanque when I can, since I am a member of The English Petanque Association.

What's your preferred home cooked meal?
I love my wife's cooking because she's Portuguese and has worked for 12 years in Italian restaurants, so she combines her Portuguese knowledge with the Italian dishes and when she cooks it's with passion and that always reflects in her dishes! And also because I get a night off cooking!!!

Jerome Dehoux

Chez Jerome

In The Kitchen

Ingredients - Serves 4
- 4 Duck Breasts on the bone
- 4 large Potatoes
- 1 Celeriac
- 1 Fennel
- 100ml Duck or Chicken Stock
- 2 tbsp Cranberry Jelly
- Sprig of Thyme
- 50g Butter
- 1 tbsp Brown Sugar
- 1 shot of Pernod
- 12 Cherry Tomatoes

Method
1. Peel and thinly slice the celeriac and place into a shallow baking tray. Add a thin layer of water then add the butter, brown sugar, thyme and season with sea salt. Heat on the hob for approximately 10 minutes until the celeriac is soft.
2. Peel the potatoes and trim to create an oval shape and poach in boiling water (starting from cold) for approximately five minutes or until soft.
3. Mix the stock with the cranberry jelly until it forms a thin paste.
4. Take the duck breast and slice the skin to expose the fat and season with salt and pepper. Pan fry the duck with the skin side down with no oil using a low heat. Gently increase the heat and seal the duck on both sides. Remove the excess fat and then cook in the oven for about 15 minutes at 180ºC.
5. Poach the fennel for around 10 minutes in boiling water. Add the Pernod and season with sea salt. When cooked slice in half. A few minutes before removing the duck from the oven add the cherry tomatoes. When cooked allow the duck 2-3 minutes to rest before serving.
6. Gently melt some butter in a pan until it forms a rich foam then add the potatoes, celeriac and fennel.
7. Slice the duck and drizzle the cranberry sauce on the top, garnish with the thyme.

Seared Duck Breast with Cranberry Sauce

Chef Profile

Describe your style of cooking
Fresh, seasonal, simple and tasty.

Training and brackground
I've been running The Crooked Billet for 12 years; worked in London, Barbados, Italy and Cambridge.

What do you love most about your job?
There are lots of things I love about my job; producing lovely food, knowing that people are enjoying all your hard work.

What prompted you to become a Chef?
Delia Smith! Yes, I know. I knew from the age of 9 and never changed my mind, giving dinner parties to my poor grandparents.

Which seasonal produce do you look forward to?
I love the summer season (when we get it). Beautiful tomatoes, British raspberries and strawberries, herbs, fresh earthy flavours.

How do you like to unwind?
After work; a movie and a glass of wine. If I get more time off; a walk on the beach in Heacham with my parents and husband.

What's your preferred home cooked meal?
Anything my husband cooks for me when we have a night off together.

Do you have a favourite cook book?
I love cook books, I have over 100, so choosing a favourite one is difficult but at the moment I would say I'm loving "Ripailles" by Stephane Reynaud.

Emma Gilchrist

In The Kitchen

Ingredients - Serves 4 - *Prepared the day before so no prep the day of a dinner party*
- 1 large Carrot (roughly chopped)
- 1 Onion (roughly chopped)
- Few Celery Sticks (roughly chopped)
- 2 Garlic Cloves (smashed)
- Sprig Fresh Thyme
- 2 Bay Leaves
- 500ml Good Quality Cider
- Small Splash Cider Vinegar, plus extra to season
- 1 ltr Fresh Chicken Stock
- 1.2kg piece un-scored Boneless Pork Belly
- 2tbsp Sunflower Oil

Method

1 Heat oven to 180C/160C fan/gas 4. Place all the ingredients except the pork and sunflower oil in a flameproof pan that will fit the pork snugly - a casserole dish is ideal. Season, bring everything to the boil then turn down the heat and slide the pork into the pan. The pork should be totally submerged - if it isn't, top up with water. Cover the dish with a lid or tight tent of foil and place it in the oven for 3 hrs undisturbed.

2 When the pork is cooked, leave it to cool slightly in the stock. When cool, take the pork out of the dish and place on a tray. Weigh the pork down with another dish or some cans and leave to cool in the fridge overnight. Strain the juices into a jug or small saucepan, cover and chill.

3 Trim the uneven edges so that you have a neat sheet of meat. Cut the meat into 4 equal pieces and set aside until ready to cook. Lift off any bits of fat from the braising juices and tip what will now be jelly into a saucepan, then bubble down by about two-thirds until starting to become slightly syrupy. Add a few more drops of vinegar, to taste. Heat the oil in a large frying pan until hot, then turn the heat down. Add the pork to the pan, skin-side down - be careful as it has a tendency to spit. Sizzle the pork as you would bacon for 5 mins until the skin is crisp. Flip it over and cook for 3-4 mins until browned. Drizzle over the reduced cooking liquor/sauce and serve.

Chef Profile

Describe your style of cooking
A mixture of classic French and British with a twist.

Current speciality
I am a lifelong fish lover, so our sea bass with vegetable spaghetti and brown shrimp butter is a current favourite.

Training and brackground
After spending 10 years training and working in France, I came to England and have worked in a number of country house hotels before joining Woburn.

What do you love most about your job?
The creativity and freedom I have working at Woburn.

What prompted you to become a Chef?
My mother and grandmother were very inspiring cooks and my earliest and happiest memories of childhood are of being in the kitchen with them.

Which seasonal produce do you look forward to?
I just love the versatility of asparagus and of course its flavour.

What's your preferred home cooked meal?
I love steak tartare, but actually always cook it at home myself, (despite my wife Samantha being a fabulous cook too!)

Do you have a favourite cook book?
My all time favourite book that I revisit time after time is "Nico" by Nico Landenis. My copy is well worn - but I just always seem to find inspiration when I leaf through it.

Olivier Bertho

Olivier's Restaurant, The Inn at Woburn

In The Kitchen

Ingredients - Serves 4

For the Rhubarb Purée:
• Boiron Rhubarb Purée
• Sugar to sweeten
• Grenadine
• Red food colouring

For the Custard Cream:
• 500g Milk
• 200g Egg Yolk
• 50g Sugar
• 2 tbsp Cornflour
• Vanilla seeds
• Whipped cream
• Meringue nests

For the Glass Tuille:
• Rhubarb and custard boiled sweets

Method

1 *For the Rhubarb Purée:* Put purée in a saucepan, add sugar and grenadine to taste. Add a little red food colouring to make it go a nice bright colour. Bring to the boil and reduce a little bit to make it thicker and sweeter. Leave to cool. Place in a squeezy bottle.

2 *For the Custard Cream:* Place everything in a saucepan and mix gently until thick and creamy. Leave to cool. Once cooled, fold in some whipped cream. Place in a piping bag and leave to set. Break up some meringue nests and have ready in a sealed container.

3 *For the Glass Tuille:* Place two sweets onto a sil-pat mat and put in the oven for 5 minutess at 180°C. Once melted, take out of the oven and using a dessert spoon drag the melted sweet upwards, creating a flame effect. Take the mat off the tray and leave to cool completely before taking them off the tray.

4 *To serve:* In a tall glass dish, layer up the rhubarb, meringue and custard alternately. At the top, pipe some whipped cream and place the tuille on the top.

Rhubarb and Custard Eaton Mess

Chef Profile

Describe your style of cooking
Modern British.

Current speciality
Slow cooked pork belly, it is such a versatile dish.

Training and brackground
I started working as a kitchen porter straight after school. In 2001 started taking a real interest in food, worked at Le Manoir Aux Quat Saisons for two years and then went on to work for John Burton-Race and Jean Christophe Novelli.

What do you love most about your job?
I have the freedom to write my own menus.

Which seasonal produce do you look forward to?
Summer Berries.

What's your favourite food combo?
Meat and fish i.e. Pork Belly and Scallops.

How do you like to unwind?
I love taking my dog on long walks and spending time with my wife.

What's your preferred home cooked meal?
My wife's Spaghetti Bolognese.

Do you have a favourite cook book?
"White Heat", Marco Pierre White.

Stuart James

In The Kitchen

Ingredients - Serves 4
- 2 x 250g Monkfish Tails (filleted)
- 2 tbsp Groundnut Oil
- 1 small Red Pepper (thinly sliced)
- 1 small Yellow Pepper (thinly sliced)
- 1 small Shallot (thinly sliced)
- 1 tbsp Chopped Ginger
- 1 small Courgette (sliced)
- 120g Pak Choi (shredded)
- 50g Fresh Beansprouts
- 2 tbsp Light Soy Sauce
- 1½tsp Chilli
- 1 tsp Sesame Oil
- Salt & Pepper to taste
- Lemon Vinaigrette

Method
1 Remove any grey membrane from the Monkfish and cut into 1½" slices.
2 Prepare all other ingredients before you start cooking.
3 Heat a large wok until almost smoking. Add one tablespoon of the oil and stir-fry the Monkfish for about three minutes until browned on both sides. Remove and drain on paper towels and keep warm.
4 Add the remaining oil, reheat, stir-fry the peppers, onion, ginger and courgette for two minutes until coloured lightly. Remove from the wok with a draining spoon and keep warm.
5 Reheat the wok and stir-fry the pak choi and beansprouts for two minutes then add the chilli. Return the other vegetables to the wok, toss in the sesame oil and reheat until very hot. Season with salt and pepper.
6 Divide among four warmed plates and arrange the Monkfish on top, trickle a little lemon vinaigrette on the top of each portion, then serve.

Chef Profile

Describe your style of cooking
I cook all different types of cuisine, originally being taught classical French which I still use in a lot of my cooking!

Current speciality
Seafood Gratin - Mussels, Prawns, Smoked Salmon, Cod and Haddock in a creamy white wine, mixed herb and parmesan sauce finished under the grill with a petite salad and crusty bread.

Training and brackground
4 years under Peter Chandler at "Paris House", 3 years at Jean Christophe-Novelli's "White Horse" at Harpenden and "French Horn" at Steppingley, eventually as his Head Chef. Then on to "The Plough" at Wavendon as Head Chef, where I gained 2 Rosettes.

What do you love most about your job?
Cooking great food and never having a day the same!!

What prompted you to become a Chef?
Having an interest in food and the ability to create anything you like!

Which seasonal produce do you look forward to?
Berries and Rhubarb, and especially Wood Sorrel and Hedge Garlic.

What's your favourite food combo?
Pork belly and Lobster.

How do you like to unwind?
Eating out and Fishing.

What's your preferred home cooked meal?
Lasagne and Salad.

Do you have a favourite cook book?
Noma - Rene Redzepi.

Chris Smith

The Three Tuns

In The Kitchen

Ingredients

- 1 Halibut Fillet
- 300g Pappardelle Pasta
- 200g Chicken Jus
- 100g Whipping Cream
- 20ml White Truffle Oil
- 100g Flat Leaf Parsley
- 1kg Oxtail Knuckles
- 1 Carrot
- 2 Onions
- 200ml Red Wine
- 1 ltr Chicken Stock
- 1 Lemon

Method

1 Roast off and season oxtail in a roasting pan, add diced carrot and onion, red wine and chicken stock and slowly simmer for 4-5 hours or until the oxtail becomes tender, strain and pick the meat off the oxtail.

2 Boil pasta in salted water, once cooked drain and drizzle with olive oil.

3 Heat up chicken jus and whipping cream, bring to the boil and reduce by a 1/3 and add your picked oxtail, white truffle, seasoning and chopped parsley.

4 Pan fry the Halibut fillet, add lemon juice and finish in the oven for 2-3 minutes.

5 Add the Pappardelle to the white truffle cream (café au lait) and place in the bottom of a bowl, place the cooked halibut on top, finish with a sprig of parsley and a wedge of lemon.

The Perfect Surf n Turf!!

Seared Halibut, Braised Oxtail Pappardelle in a Café au Lait & White Truffle Sauce

The Kings Head, Ivinghoe

Chef Profile

Describe your style of cooking
Modern English and a few of the classical dishes.

Current speciality
Aylesbury Duckling cooked traditionally and our new tasting menu.

Training and brackground
Trainee chef at the King's Head, Ivinghoe; Grosvenor House, Park Lane; Randolph Hotel, Oxford; Senior Sous Chef, Pendley Manor Hotel, Tring; Le Belle Epoque, South Kensington, Sous Chef; Brocket Hall, Hertfordshire, Head Chef; Auberge du Lac, Hertfordshire, Senior Sous Chef and back to the King's Head, Ivinghoe as Head Chef and one of the three owners.

What do you love most about your job?
The service – seeing the food go out to the guests as perfect as possible (and seeing the empty plates come back!)

What prompted you to become a Chef?
My father, who was a great chef and inspiration.

Which seasonal produce do you look forward to?
English asparagus, peas and berries.

How do you like to unwind?
Spending time with my 2 children, eating and drinking, going to the gym.

What's your preferred home cooked meal?
Christmas dinner cooked by my mother.

Jonathan O'Keeffe

In The Kitchen

Ingredients
- Zest and Juice of 2 ½ Lemons
- 4 Whole Eggs
- 1 Egg Yolk
- 175g Sugar

For the pastry:
- 250g Flour
- 125g Butter at room temperature
- 65g Icing Sugar
- 2 Egg Yolks
- 1/2 tbsp Double Cream

Method
1 *For the pastry:* Beat the butter and icing sugar until smooth.
2 Beat in the egg yolks, then flour and double cream until a pastry is formed.
3 Knead into a ball, cover with cling film and place in fridge for 1 hour to rest.
4 Roll pastry on a floured surface to form a 12" circle.
5 Line a buttered 8" tart ring with the pastry and trim off edges. Bake blind for 25 mins at 350°F, then remove baking beans and cook for a further 5 mins.
6 *For the lemon filling:* Whisk the eggs, egg yolk, sugar, cream, juice and zest of lemons until smooth and strain through a sieve.
7 Pour the mixture into the tart mould and bake for 30 mins at 175°F.
8 Check often towards the end of cooking time – the tart should have a little "wobble" in the middle.
9 Cool for 1 hour and serve with whipped cream and seasonal berries.

Lemon Tart

Chef Profile

Describe your style of cooking
My cuisine is unpretentious and modern in its approach but developed from my classical French training. I try to think outside the box. At Cameron's I have created a traditional yet innovative style with a genuine commitment to local produce.

Current speciality
I have just bought a smoker for the restaurant so at the moment I am experimenting a lot with that, creating lots of home-smoked foods. Some of the foods I have trialled on the menu include home-smoked scallops, home-smoked cheeses and home-smoked strawberries.

What do you love most about your job?
The real thrill of the job is the feedback from customers. After a long, hard service nothing beats hearing how much your customers enjoyed themselves.

What prompted you to become a Chef?
I've always enjoyed cooking and even as a child experimented with food. Whilst taking my A-levels I almost fell in to a job as a Chef, I found I had a natural talent for cooking, so decided to make a career of it.

Which seasonal produce do you look forward to?
I love cooking Game, its quality produce like this that inspires me with my cooking. Any dish must do the produce justice.

How do you like to unwind?
I love being outdoors and have two dogs and so enjoy relaxing by taking them for long walks. I am lucky to live with so many great walks on my doorstep. When I get the chance I enjoy foraging with them, it's a great way to mix work with pleasure!

Do you have a favourite cook book?
Having trained at Leith's school of Cookery and Wine, I would have to say that their Cookery Bible is my favourite cook book.

Dan Cameron

Cameron's Brasserie

In The Kitchen

Ingredients - Serves 4
- 225g Raspberries
- 120g Egg white
- 100g Caster Sugar
- 15ml Lemon Juice
- 10g Cornflour, dissolved in 1 tablespoon of water

Method
1 Butter and sugar a soufflé mould and place in fridge.
2 Cook raspberries in a pan with half the sugar and half the lemon juice for a couple of minutes. Blend and sieve so you are left with a coulis.
3 Add cornflour to the coulis to thicken it.
4 Whisk egg whites gradually adding the sugar till at medium peak. Add the lemon juice at the end.
5 Gently fold the coulis and meringue together. Divide between the surface soufflé dishes. Smooth the top and run your thumb round the edge to give a top hat effect.
6 Bake at 180°c for 10 minutes.
7 Dust with icing sugar and serve immediately.

Easy Hot Raspberry Soufflé

Chef Profile

Describe your style of cooking
A fusion with strong Creole, French and Eastern influences to create flavoursome and vibrant dishes. I also love to cook "Classics" with a twist. My style is to create an experience on a plate for every single customer.

Current speciality
I currently do not have a speciality. Here at Beckworth, our menu changes daily which gives me the opportunity to work with a variety of fresh ingredients.

Training and brackground
I have mainly taught myself through observation, research and working in all sections of a kitchen up and down the country.

What do you love most about your job?
Being able to use the freshest, local ingredients most of which our customers can see in our food hall and produce market to cook exciting dishes. Also the freedom to be as creative as I want.

What prompted you to become a Chef?
My profession chose me – I had no control over it! I'm the happiest in a kitchen as my passion for food started from a very early age.

Which seasonal produce do you look forward to?
Nothing springs to mind - probably because I'm quite happy working with whatever is available.

What's your preferred home cooked meal?
Any good old delicious Creole dish such as spicy grilled fish with rice and a golden apple salad.

Do you have a favourite cook book?
I do, it's a very old Creole cookbook, a joint effort of four chef's, called "Gastronomie des seychelles" which is written in French!

Dominique Chang-Time

In The Kitchen

Ingredients - Serves 4

For the Cod:
- 1 Cod Fillet (cut into 4)
- Gound Black Pepper
- 4 pinches Garlic Powder
- Pinch of Nutmeg
- 100ml Vegetable Oil for frying
- 500g Spinach
- 50g Butter
- 8 Vine Cherry Tomatoes

For Butternut Squash Purée:
- 1 Butternut Squash (peeled & cubed)
- Salt & Pepper
- ½ tsp Cumin
- 1 tsp Ground Coriander
- 1tsp Olive Oil
- Juice of ½ Lime

For Red Pepper Coulis:
- Salt & Ground Pepper
- 1 Red Pepper

For Fondant Potatoes:
- 4 Large Potatoes
- 50g Butter
- 500ml Vegetable Stock
- 2 Sprigs of Thyme
- Salt & Ground Pepper

- ½ Onion
- Small Bunch of Parsley
- 1 Sprig of Thyme
- 1 tbsp Tomato Puree
- 1 tbsp Castor Sugar
- Juice of ½ Lemon
- 25ml Water
- 1cm Fresh Ginger
- ½ Chilli

Method

1 Peel potatoes, cut edges into smooth, flat surfaces. Using a metal ring push down on larger surface to cut out 4 cylinder shapes, trim each one until you have equal sizes. Wash and place in roasting tin. **2** Melt butter into hot vegetable stock. Season potatoes with salt and pepper. Add thyme. Pour mixture into baking tin and cover with foil. Place in pre-heated oven (160ºC) for 45 mins. **3** After 45 mins take off foil and leave to roast for further 10-15 mins. Remove and set aside. **4** Whilst potatoes are cooking, place butternut squash in boiling water for 20 mins or until soft but firm. Drain and place in oven for 10 mins until dry. Transfer to food processor and blend to a smooth texture, add olive oil, salt and pepper, lime juice, coriander and cumin to taste and continue to blend until a creamy purée is achieved. Place in small bowl and set aside. **5** Place tomatoes on tray, add salt and pepper, drizzle with olive oil and place under hot grill for 10 mins. **6** For the red pepper coulis place all ingredients into jug and blend until smooth. Pass through sieve into small saucepan over low heat and reduce until it slightly thickens, whisk, set aside to cool. **7** Melt butter in a pan over low heat, add spinach with salt, pepper and nutmeg, leave to wilt, occasionally tossing the spinach. **8** Place a non-stick frying pan with vegetable oil on medium heat, season cod with salt, pepper and garlic powder on each side, once oil is hot place cod skin down into pan and cook for 3-5 mins, turn and cook for further 3-4 mins. *To serve:* Reheat potatoes and puree if necessary and arrange as shown on picture.

Chef Profile

Describe your style of cooking
Classical French techniques, accented with subtle Asian flavours.

Current speciality
"Kasundi Black Cod" - Wild Catch Alaskan Roasted Black Cod; Kaffir-Lime Tomato Curry Emulsion; Freshly Grated Coconut Rice; Coriander, Apple, Mango Salsa; Norfolk Coast Pickled Samphire.

Training and brackground
Trained at The Conrad Hilton Hotel School, four year degree Houston, Texas; worked in various fine dining outlets within hotel groups Hilton, Four Seasons and Hyatt Regency.

What do you love most about your job?
Seeing empty plates coming back into the kitchen.

Chad Rahman

What prompted you to become a Chef?
From an early age I was fascinated with food; the smells, aromas and fragrances that emanated from my mother's kitchen. My mother inspired me to pursue a career in cheffing. She is my mentor. she is a naturally gifted cook who had to satisfy a large family all with different tastes and dietary requirements.

Which seasonal produce do you look forward to?
Fresh Alphonso Mangoes - fragrant, succulent, sweet and delicious when in season.

How do you like to unwind?
Reading and listening to classical music.

Do you have a favourite cook book?
"Larousse Gastronomique" (the bible of French cooking) - great bedside reading!

Chez Mumtaj

In The Kitchen

Ingredients - Serves 4

- 4 x 165g Black Cod (scaled, filleted and pin boned)
- 4 x Soft Shell Crab (dusted in seasoned potato flour and deep fried)
- 1 tsp Kasundi Mustard
- Salt & Coarse Black Pepper
- Jaggery
- Chopped Shallots
- Coriander Chopped
- Mango

- Shredded Braeburn Apple Julienne Cut
- Red & Green Pepper Julienne Cut
- Chat Masala
- Vanilla Syrup
- Pickled Samphire
- Fresh Lime
- 1 tsp Kashmiri Chilli Powder
- 1 tsp Curry Powder
- Kaffir Lime Leaves
- 1 Stem Lemongrass

- 6 Vine Cherry Tomatoes
- 1 tbsp Tomato Purée
- 1 tsp Ginger Garlic Paste
- Coconut Milk
- Micro Leaves
- Garlic-Chive Herb Butter
- Olive Oil
- 150ml Black Cod Fish Stock
- Red Onion
- Diced Butter

Method

Black Cod: Season black cod with salt & pepper. Heat frying pan, add 1 tbsp oil and bring to temperature. Place flesh side down to caramelise the protein of the cod. Then turn skin side down. Cook for 3 mins each side, add 2 knobs of butter and baste. Spread 1 tsp of kasundi mustard on flesh side then place in pre-heated oven at 220°c and oven bake for 10-12 mins. Probe fish with temperature probe. Take reading, must be 80°c plus to be fully cooked. Remove from oven and set aside, cover loosely with foil paper.

Tomato-Kaffir Lime Curry Emulsion:
1 Heat saucepan with 1 tbsp of oil and bring to temperature. **2** Add chopped shallots and ginger-garlic paste, cook out for 2 mins on low heat to soften. **3** Add ½ tsp of Kashmiri chilli, ½ tsp curry powder, salt, tomato purée, chopped vine tomatoes, jaggery, batons of lemongrass, fish stock, lime juice and Kaffir lime leaves. **4** Cook gently on low heat for 6-8 mins, add 2 knobs of butter and coconut milk to enrich to a glossy sauce. **5** Strain sauce with conical strainer and keep warm.

Coriander, Apple and Mango Salsa:
In a bowl, add shredded fresh mango, julienne cut apples, chopped coriander, sliced red onion, mixed red & green julienne cut peppers, juice of ½ lime, sprinkling of chaat powder and 1 tbsp of vanilla syrup and gently mix all the ingredients.
Plating: **1** Place 2 heaped tbsp of the salsa in the centre of the plate. Place pickled samphire on top of salsa. **2** Place black cod on top of pickled samphire skin side down. **3** Pour Tomato-Kafir Lime Sauce in ramekin. **4** Garnish fish with herb butter and micro salad leaves.

Kasundi Black Cod

The Bricklayers Arms

Pan Fried King Scallops with Parsnip Purée and Crispy Bacon

Chef Profile

Describe your style of cooking
Classic English, French Fusion.

Current speciality
No speciality as I would rather try all aspects of cooking. However, I follow any traditional British food with a twist.

Training and brackground
Two months part-time at a restaurant before two years at West Kingsway College, then 5 years of full time work.

What do you love most about your job?
The creativity I have with using different products and experimenting with seasonal produce.

What prompted you to become a Chef?
At a young age watching and helping my Mum cook.

Which seasonal produce do you look forward to?
I love looking forward to the Game season in particular.

What's your favourite food combo?
I really enjoy the softness of a pork belly with crispy crackling and a sweet sauce.

How do you like to unwind?
Cycling around the countryside.

What's your preferred home cooked meal?
A good fresh homemade burger.

Martin West

In The Kitchen

Ingredients - Serves 4
- 250g Parsnips
- 100ml Balsamic Vinegar
- 100ml Double Cream
- Milk
- 15g Butter
- 12 Fresh King Scallops
- 4 Rashers of Bacon

Pre-heat oven to 160°C

Method

1 *For the Purée:* Peel the parsnips, then top and tail them. Place them into the milk and bring them to the boil. Once the parsnips are cooked thoroughly, drain the milk and put the parsnips into a food processor. Blitz them until they become a smooth texture, then add the cream and season with salt to taste.

2 *For the Bacon:* Place the bacon onto a baking tray and into a fan assisted oven for 15 minutes. Take it out and drain the water. Place it back for another five minutes, then drain any other excess water, then cut each rasher into three even sizes.

3 *For the Scallops:* Dry the scallops on a cloth and then with a small knife, take off the tough muscle on the side of the scallop. Heat up your pan to a very hot temperature, then add the butter, then the scallops. Colour the scallops on both sides to give them a nice caramelised look. Place them into the oven for two minutes and then season them just before serving, not before, as this will break the protein in the scallops.

4 *For the Balsamic Glaze:* Boil the vinegar until it reduces to a thick syrup consistency. You can flavour your glaze to your taste using any sweet condiment such as honey or plum sauce.

5 *To serve:* Making sure all the aspects are hot, put the balsamic glaze onto the plate, then using a teaspoon put three quenelles of the purée on top. Next, place the bacon slightly off centre on the purée and finally put one scallop on each quenelle of purée.

behind the scenes

Chef Profile

Describe your style of cooking
Modern and Classical British Cuisine with International influence.

Current speciality
Using the produce from Claydon's kitchen garden.

Training and brackground
Top hotels in London and ending the training at The Montreux Palace, Switzerland. Head Chef RAC Club, Pall Mall, The London Stock Exchange, Langan's and Rosamund the Fair, Oxford's famous cruising restaurant.

What do you love most about your job?
As Chef/Proprietor I enjoy being in total control of the produce we use at The Carriage House Restaurant and working within such beautiful surroundings. Claydon is a gem.

What prompted you to become a Chef?
I had a passionate desire to be a chef from the age of five when I baked my first cake.

Which seasonal produce do you look forward to?
Mushrooms! We host a Mushroom Foray with John Wright from The River Cottage every Autumn. It's just like a treasure hunt. One year our baskets were laden with Hedgehog Mushrooms that are delicious on toast with a simple garlic butter.

How do you like to unwind?
Spending time with my family. We know a beautiful quiet spot close to home where we swim in the river and BBQ.

What's your preferred home cooked meal?
My wife's Chicken Soup.

Do you have a favourite cook book?
"THE flavour THESAURUS" by Niki Segnit. Invaluable!

Tim Matthews _____

The Carriage House Restaurant, Claydon House

In The Kitchen

Ingredients - Serves 4
- 4 Hake Fillets approx 150-200g each
- Fennel Mash
- 600ml Vegetable Stock
- 200g Garden Peas
- 200g Broad Beans
- 200g Crème Fraiche
- 4 tbsp Chopped Fresh Mint
- 1 tsp Mint Sauce

Method
1. Bring stock, peas and broad beans to boil and simmer for 15 minutes. Season. Pass through fine sieve.
2. Make mash for four. Gently cook half a blub of medium diced fresh fennel in a little olive oil for 5 minutes and add to mash.
3. Season and flour hake fillets. Heat olive oil in pan and add fillets. Cook for 5 - 7 minutes on each side until just cooked through.
4. Serve in deep bowls, fennel mash in ball at base, hake on top, broth around the base of dish and teaspoon of mint crème fraiche on top. Garnish with fennel sprig.

Fillet of Hake with a Fennel Mash, Pea Broth and Mint Crème Fraiche

Roade House Restaurant & Hotel

Anytime "Breakfast"

Chef Profile

Describe your style of cooking
Modern British.

Current speciality
Grilled fillet of mackerel with beetroot salad and preserved lemon relish.

Training and brackground
Self taught.

What do you love most about your job?
After 30 years I still get a buzz when things work.

What prompted you to become a Chef?
Failed at everything else - intrigued by the theatrical element of restaurants.

Which seasonal produce do you look forward to?
Game season.

How do you like to unwind?
I am a very keen road cyclist.

What's your preferred home cooked meal?
Roast pork.

Do you have a favourite cook book?
Diana Henry, "Crazy Water, Pickled Lemons".

Chris Kewley

In The Kitchen

Ingredients - Serves 1
- 1 Egg
- 1 Cooking Chorizo
- 1 Small Onion
- 1 Garlic Clove
- 1 Slice of Thick Bread
- Various Mushrooms
- A few Herbs
- 1 small can Plum Tomatoes
- Butter

Method
1. Chop onion and garlic and reduce to a thick compote with tomatoes.
2. Brush bread with olive oil and garlic.
3. Slice chorizo lengthways into three and grill.
4. Poach egg in simmering water.
5. Pan fry mushrooms in butter with some garlic and lemon juice.
6. Cut a nice centre out of the toasted bread.
7. Place tomato mixture on top, put grilled chorizo on top of that and finally add the poached egg.
8. Scatter the mushrooms around the crouton and drizzle chorizo oil with chopped herbs on top.
9. Make as a starter or tasty snack.

behind the scenes

Chef Profile

Describe your style of cooking
Modern seasonal British with international and classical influences.

Current speciality
The dish I'm most proud of on the menu currently is Cotswold White Chicken with Pancetta and Shallot Stuffing, Apricot Purée, Morel Mushrooms, Jersey Royal Potatoes and Evesham Asparagus.

Training and brackground
I have spent 13 years working in various hotels and restaurants in the UK and overseas, and was most recently at Fawsley Hall Hotel, 3 AA rosettes, and before that at the Dormy House Hotel in Broadway, 2 AA rosettes, as well as Brocket Hall.

What do you love most about your job?
The knowledge to present one ingredient in different textures, combinations with flavours and visual theatre on the plate.

What prompted you to become a Chef?
Both of my parents are good cooks, and using fresh, seasonal and organic ingredients at home helped me understand how important that is for the food and finished product.

Which seasonal produce do you look forward to?
Artichoke (Globe and Jerusalem).

What's your favourite food combo?
My favourite food combo is John Dory and braised chicken oysters.

What's your preferred home cooked meal?
A big bowl of Mussels Mariniere with fresh crusty bread – perfect!

Do you have a favourite cook book?
The French Laundry by Thomas Keller, he has a reputation for his culinary skills and high standards, and for being the only American chef to hold multiple three star Michelin ratings, and Alinea by Grant Achatz.

Damyan Stefanov

Murrays at Whittlebury Hall

In The Kitchen

Ingredients - Serves 4
- Salmon (Loch Duart)
  4 pieces fillet about 50g trimmed of skin
- 20g Keta Caviar (washed)
- 20g Avruga Caviar
- 200g Jersey Royal Potatoes
- 20g Chives (finely chopped)
- 50ml Sugar Syrup
- 2g Xanthan Gum
- 4 Lemons
- 1 ltr Vegetable Oil (for cooking the salmon)
- Edible flowers for decoration

Method
1 *For the salmon mi-cuit:* Clean and trim the salmon, removing all bones, using a sharp knife remove fillet from the skin.
2 Portion the salmon into 50g pieces (barrel shape).
3 Fill the oil bath or pan with vegetable oil and bring up to 48°c (if you're using a pan with oil regulate the temperature carefully).
4 Place the salmon into the oil bath for 20 minutes, remove and drain on a clean cloth, and season with Maldon sea salt and white pepper.
5 *For the potatoes:* Scrub the muddy potatoes under cold water. Boil them until tender (approximately 10 minutes). Once cooked, drain and cool slightly before cutting them into a square shape (2x2cm).
6 *For the lemon gel:* Peel the lemons using a kitchen peeler, reserve the lemons. Place the lemon skin into a pan with cold water and bring it to the boil, once boiling change the water with fresh, repeat this another 10 times (this takes out the bitter flavour of the lemons).
7 Drain the lemon zest and place them in a fast speed food blender together with juice from one lemon, sugar syrup and the xanthan gum. Once blended, pass through a fine strainer.

Organic Salmon with Lemon, Jersey Royal

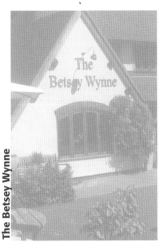

Chef Profile

Describe your style of cooking
Old fashioned English, using modern locally grown produce.

Current speciality
Our own breed meats, 'proper' pies, simple presentation.

Training and brackground
Thomas Danby College, Leeds. C & G Standard. Owned The Royal Oak, East Lavant, and worked at The Glynebourne. Head Chef at The Betsey Wynne for five years and Landlord for three years.

What do you love most about your job?
Variety of work, several challenges and achieving high compliment ratio.

What prompted you to become a Chef?
It was an ambition from an early age.

Which seasonal produce do you look forward to?
The berry season from our own gardens.

What's your favourite food combo?
A trio of Salmon, Prawns and Sole Fillets with a rich shellfish broth.

How do you like to unwind?
I play league snooker every week and enjoy being competitive.

What's your preferred home cooked meal?
Fresh local pork loin, Sunday style.

Do you have a favourite cook book?
"The Essential Mosimann".

Kevin Close

In The Kitchen

Ingredients - Serves 2
- 500ml Chicken Stock
- 220g Prawns - shell on
- 220g Crab Legs
- 70g Fresh Ginger
- 1 Whole Lime
- 1 Lemongrass Stick
- 2 tbsp Thai Fish Sauce
- 2 Egg Whites
- 150g Julienne of Leeks
- 200g Glass Noodles
- 360g Fresh Cod
- 1 Bok Choi
- Sesame Oil

Pre-heat oven 375°F/190°C/Gas 5

Method
1. Add to chicken stock; fresh ginger, lemongrass, lime zest and juice, chillies to taste, crab legs and prawn shells (if available). Cook gently for 20 minutes.
2. Strain into clean pan. Remove meat from claws and set aside.
3. Add chopped chives and egg whites, whisk and bring gently to the boil, simmer for five minutes. Strain through a muslin cloth.
4. Add to hot stock; peeled raw prawns, after five minutes add the leeks and bok choi, remove from heat and drain when cooked. Cook noodles in boiling water and drain. Sear cod in sesame oil skin side down and place in hot oven for six minutes. Rest fish for three minutes.
5. *To serve:* Assemble ingredients in bowl with noodles, then the leeks and bok choi and then add the prawns, place the cod gently on the top, skin side up. Pour over the prepared stock and finish with a sprinkle of the crab flakes and coriander.

Chef Profile

Describe your style of cooking
Simple seasonal ingredients, strong powerful flavours. Modern techniques.

Current speciality
Pure Breed 60 day aged Local Beef, Globe Artichokes, Wild Mushrooms, Foyot, Port Sauce.

Training and brackground
Started in kitchens on the Isle of Wight aged 13. I did a lot of Stages in my mid 20's whilst working, training apprentice Chefs and teaching WSET wine courses.

What do you love most about your job?
Working with suppliers to create the best produce. Building blocks if you like.

What prompted you to become a Chef?
Rolling croissants aged 8 in a tiny bakery on the Dordogne River.

Which seasonal produce do you look forward to?
The local Asparagus, local soft fruits, anything homegrown brought in by customers.

What's your favourite food combo?
Scallops and cauliflower.

How do you like to unwind?
Eating out with my other half Sophie and 4 year old daughter Olivia. Top critics!

What's your preferred home cooked meal?
It's probably most people's favourite; a good Sunday lunch.

Do you have a favourite cook book?
"Ripailles" by Stephane Reynaud or "Roast Chicken & Other Stories" by Simon Hopkinson.

Jon Adriaenssens

Bell & Bear

In The Kitchen

Ingredients - Serves 4
- 4 pieces fresh skinned Cod (about 150-200g each)
- 200g Duck Fat
- Sea Salt
- Peppercorns
- Star Anise
- 200g Marsh Samphire (washed)
- 16 Cherry Tomatoes
- 100ml Rapeseed Oil (British Cold Pressed)
- 30ml Sherry Vinegar
- Juice of one Lime
- Juice of half an Orange
- 1 tsp Icing Sugar
- 1 tsp Dijon Mustard
- 1 Garlic Clove (pressed / puree)
- Knob of Butter
- Pea Shoots to garnish

Method
1. The day before, salt the cod lightly with Maldon or Cornish Sea Salt and cover in the fridge.
2. When ready to cook; make the dressing by combining oil, juice of lime, juice of orange, mustard, garlic, vinegar and sugar and whisking together until emulsified.
3. Melt the duck fat in a saucepan with a few peppercorns and some star anise then heat to 60°c (use a needle probe to test the temperature) submerge the cod in the fat. Cook in the fat at 60°c for 12 minutes, the fish should be just between jellied and flaky. Regulate the heat by taking the pan on and off the heat.
4. Sauté cherry tomatoes in foaming butter for a couple of minutes, add the samphire, and cook until softened. Drain well on kitchen paper and season.
5. To plate; put the samphire and tomatoes on a warm serving plate. Drain the fish and lay atop the samphire, drizzle over the emulsified dressing and garnish with some pea shoots, serve with a side dish of buttered new potatoes.

Confit of Cod Loin, Samphire, Pan Roast Tomatoes, Citrus Vinaigrette

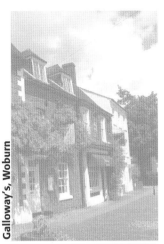

Galloway's, Woburn

Chef Profile

Training and brackground
I have worked at Galloway's for 15 years, where I gained NVQ's 2 & 3 through an apprenticeship.

What do you love most about your job?
Knowing the customers have had a good meal.

What prompted you to become a Chef?
A weekend job washing up in a pub as a teenager.

Which seasonal produce do you look forward to?
Summer produce, when the English strawberries and raspberries are at their best.

What's your favourite food combo?
Blue cheese and bacon.

How do you like to unwind?
I watch a lot of films and I'm a fan of live music and stand-up comedy.

What's your preferred home cooked meal?
Sausage and mash with onion gravy.

Do you have a favourite cook book?
"Rhodes Around Britain" - it has an amazing dessert section.

Kevin Newell

In The Kitchen

Ingredients
- 9oz Plain Flour
- 4½oz Cocoa Powder
- 3 tsp Baking Powder
- 12oz Softened Butter
- 1½lb Soft Brown Sugar
- 1½ tsp Vanilla Essence

Method
1. Sieve together the flour, cocoa powder and baking powder.
2. Cream together the butter, sugar and vanilla essence until light and fluffy.
3. Add to the butter mix in the eggs one at a time.
4. Fold in the dry ingredients.
5. Place into a lined baking tray.
6. Cook in a pre-heated oven on 180ºC / 350ºF or gas mark 4 for approx 30 to 40 minutes.
7. Serve warm with vanilla ice cream and chocolate sauce.

Chocolate Brownie

Chef Profile

Describe your style of cooking
French English Fusion.

Current speciality
Roasted Squab Pigeon, Puy Lentils, Barigoule, Pomme Ana, Café au Lait.

Training and brackground
I went to Bournemouth & Poole College and completed the specialised chef scholarship before I joined Roux Fine Dining for whom I worked for 5 years. I then joined the Nags Head and have worked here for 4 years.

What do you love most about your job?
I love that every day is different and I love when one season ends and another begins.

What prompted you to become a Chef?
Cooking meals at home with my mum made me always want to be a Chef.

Which seasonal produce do you look forward to?
Game.

What's your favourite food combo?
There's something about peas and smoked bacon that I just love.

How do you like to unwind?
I like to play golf and squash.

Do you have a favourite cook book?
Between two definitely - Le Gavroche and The French Laundry.

The Nags Head, Great Missenden

Howard Gale _____

In The Kitchen

Ingredients - Serves 4
- 200g Smoked Eel Fillets
- 2 large Purple Beetroots (pickled)
- 25g Fresh Horseradish
- 1 Curly Endive Lettuce
- 12 Cherry Tomatoes
- 100g French Green Beans
- 1 Lemon
- 25ml Olive Oil
- Salt & Pepper
- Chervil and Chives for decoration

Method
1. Blanch the french beans in boiling water for about 3 minutes or until al dente, then refresh in iced water.
2. Slice one of the beetroots into 4 discs to sit the beans on and dice the other beetroot for the salad.
3. Cut the smoked eel fillets into portions so each person has 3 pieces.
4. Zest the lemon and squeeze the juice into a bowl and whisk in the olive oil a little at a time.
5. Add the diced beetroot, horseradish, chopped chives, salt & pepper to the lemon dressing and combine.
6. Arrange the disc of beetroot with the beans on top. Place some of the lettuce on top and dress with the dressing.
7. Place the eel fillet on the plate along with the sliced tomatoes.
8. Drizzle some of the beetroot dressing around the plate. Place some grated horseradish on top and garnish with Chervil.

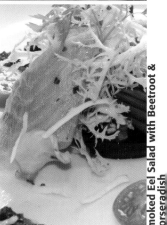

Smoked Eel Salad with Beetroot & Horseradish

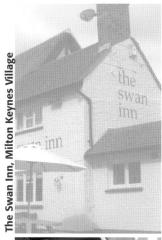

Chef Profile

Describe your style of cooking
French with a Mediterranean twist.

Current speciality
Pork Belly with Mashed Potato, Sautéed Spinach, Scotch Egg & Red Wine Sauce.

Training and brackground
French Catering College (apprenticeship). Worked at The Bell Inn and Hill House (Horndon-on-the-Hill, Essex). Worked at The Russell Arms (Butlers Cross, Bucks). Working at The Swan Inn since 2010.

What do you love most about your job?
I love using fresh and seasonal products and the freedom to create my own menus.

What prompted you to become a Chef?
My love of good food and wine.

Which seasonal produce do you look forward to?
Salmon, Trout, Rabbit, Pigeon, anything some of our local customers bring us.

How do you like to unwind?
Simply with a nice pint of real ale at the end of a long day!

What's your preferred home cooked meal?
My mums cooking (Risotto, Rabbit Braised in Cider Cream with Spaetzle).

Ben Hars

In The Kitchen

Ingredients - Serves 4

- 1-1.2kg Pork Belly (boned)
- 1 Carrot (diced)
- 1 Onion (diced)
- 1 piece of Celery (diced)
- Sprig of Rosemary
- Sprig of Thyme
- 1 Bay Leaf
- 10 Cloves
- 10g Salt
- 5 Whole Black Peppercorns
- 1 Star Anise
- 250g Baby Spinach

For the Mashed Potato:
- 4 Large Potatoes (peeled)
- 70g Butter
- 70ml Cream

For the Scotch Eggs:
- 2 Eggs
- 150g Sausagemeat
- Breadcrumbs & Flour

For the Red Wine Sauce:
- 200ml Red Wine
- 2 Shallots
- 1 Sprig of Thyme

For the Apple Sauce:
- 2 Granny Smiths
- 100ml Cloudy Apple Juice
- Olive Oil
- Salt & Pepper to taste

Pre-heat oven 190°c/Gas 6

Method

Pork Belly: **1** Peel and cut the onion in half and stud them with cloves. **2** Place the belly in a stock pan with the diced vegetables, onion, herbs and spices. **3** Fill with water with 4-5 inches over the belly, add 10g of salt. **4** Bring to the boil and gently cook until tender (roughly 1½ - 2 hours). **5** Carefully remove the belly and place between two dishes to press. Place 2kg weight on top of the plate, place in the fridge and leave until it is completely set. *Red Wine Sauce:* **1** Reduce the red wine with the shallots and herbs until there is almost no liquid remaining. **2** Add the demi glace and bring to the boil.
Apple Sauce: **1** Peel and dice the apples. **2** Cook until soft with the apple juice. **3** Place in a blender and blitz until smooth.
Scotch Eggs: **1** Place the eggs in boiling water for 6 minutes. **2** Remove from the water and cool down. **3** Peel the eggs. **4** Wrap them in sausagemeat. **5** Roll them in flour and coat in breadcrumbs. Roll them in flour again and coat in breadcrumbs once more. **6** Deep fry the scotch eggs until golden. Place in a pre-heated oven for a further 5-6 minutes.
Mashed Potato: **1** Cut potatoes into chunks and boil until soft, drain well and mash. **2** Boil the cream, butter, salt and pepper and add to mashed potatoes. *To Finish:* **1** Cut 4 equal slices of pork belly. **2** Score the top and sprinkle with salt (top only). **3** Drizzle a little oil in a hot pan and place the belly skin side down. **4** Place in the oven immediately and roast for 15 - 20 minutes (until brown & crispy). *Sauteed Spinach:* **1** Drizzle olive oil in a hot frying pan, put the spinach in the pan until wilted.

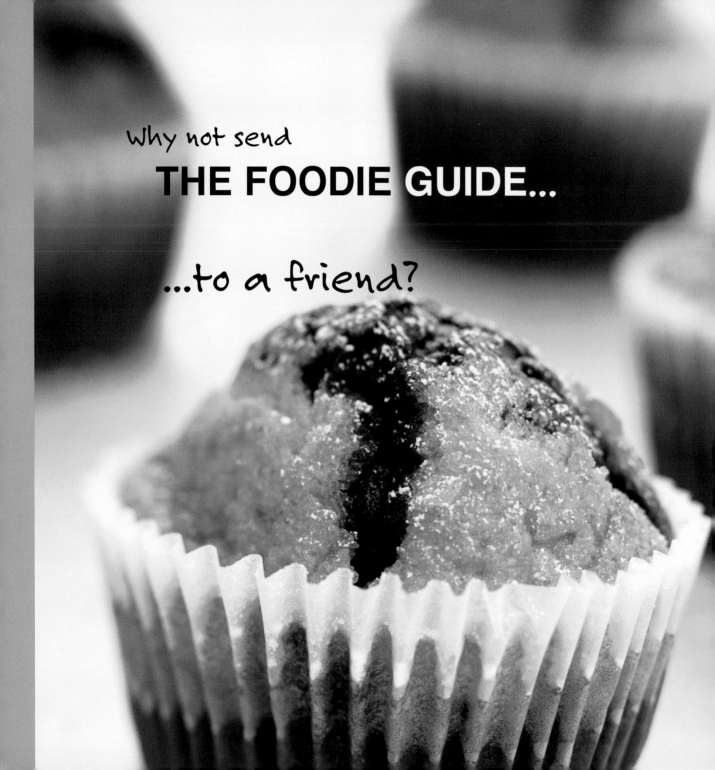

Why not send
THE FOODIE GUIDE...

...to a friend?

ORDER THE FOODIE GUIDE FOR A FRIEND

'The Perfect Gift'

> ❧ **Step 1** Fill in the name and address details of the recipient.
> ❧ **Step 2** Write your personal message (this cut out section will be enclosed with the guide).
> ❧ **Step 3** Fill in your name and address details on reverse of message section.
> ❧ **Step 4** Return completed form to us with a cheque for £6 per book (p&p FREE).
>   N.B. Guides are despatched via Royal Mail. We will send you a receipt once despatched.

Please make cheques payable to The Square Design & Print Co Ltd and post (no need for a stamp) to:-
Freepost RSKB-RHRA-RZBT, The Foodie Guide Ltd, 373 Welford Road, Northampton NN2 8PT.

❧ **Step 1**

Fill in the name and address details of the recipient.

Please post to:

Name

Address

Postcode

Write your message below and then **fill in your details on the reverse** -

we will do the rest...

❧ **Step 2**

Write your personal message (this section will be enclosed with the guide).

Your message:

THE FOODIE GUIDE

Your favourite restaurants, delis and farm shops

nt vouchers
ember 2013

'The Perfect Gift'

THE FOODIE GUIDE has been sent to you from:

Name

Address

Postcode

Tel

Email

Step 3

Fill in **your** name and address details.

Step 4

Return form with your cheque to:
Freepost RSKB-RHRA-RZBT,
The Foodie Guide Ltd,
373 Welford Road,
Northampton, NN2 8PT.

lifestyle

WOBURN
The Inn at Woburn

BOOK THE PERFECT
WEEKEND ESCAPE

Set in the heart of the Georgian village of Woburn, the hotel is owned and managed by the historic Woburn Abbey estate. With 48 bedrooms and 7 character cottages, the hotel blends the traditions of the 18th Century effortlessly with modern comforts, including our 2AA Rosette Olivier's Restaurant.

We offer a range of special breaks throughout the year. So if you simply feel like getting away from it all and enjoying a relaxing few days, The Inn at Woburn promises a great stay.

Romantic Break
from £99.50*
per person based on
two people sharing

Golfing Break
from £260.00*
per person based on
two people sharing

Sunday Supper
Night from £70.00*
per person based on two
people sharing

Gourmet Break from
£170.00* (2 night break)
per person based on
two people sharing

In addition, we offer complimentary entry into Woburn Abbey Gardens and concessionary rates for Woburn Abbey and Woburn Safari Park for all hotel guests during their stay. For further details or to book, please contact the hotel on 01525 290441 or email inn@woburn.co.uk quoting 'The Foodie Guide'.

*Full details available on website. All breaks subject to availability and based on two people sharing. Prices quoted are valid until December 2012. Please enquire for 2013 prices. Concessionary entry to Woburn Abbey, the gardens and Woburn Safari Park is subject to opening times.

George Street, Woburn, Bedfordshire, MK17 9PX
Tel: (01525) 290441 Fax: (01525) 290432 • Email: inn@woburn.co.uk
woburn.co.uk

lifestyle

morgan gilder

interiors & furniture specialists

lignet-roset

contemporary & traditional interior styling

...using the very best of design-led furniture, fabrics, wallpapers, paints & lighting

morgan gilder showroom at: 14 High Street, Stony Stratford, Milton Keynes MK11 1AF
Tel: 01908 568 674 • Fax: 01908 568 602 • Email: info@morgangilder.co.uk

www.morgangilder.co.uk

lifestyle

BEAUTIFULLY FUNCTIONAL

OLIVER | JAMES

GARDEN ROOMS

BEAUTIFUL AND FUNCTIONAL LIVING SPACES CREATED BY **OLIVER JAMES GARDEN ROOMS**

As shortlisted in the 2012 International Design & Architecture Awards

Imagine the perfect living space designed especially for you and your family - right now, in your existing home. Oliver James Garden Rooms can make this a reality. We can transform your home with a beautiful and functional Garden Room.

Why choose Oliver James Garden Rooms? We personally manage your project throughout - from initial design and planning permission, right through to build and finishing. Our team consists of locally based, but internationally recognised specialists. The very best design and technical team, builders and craftsmen will make your dreams a reality. Our immaculate attention to detail means that we excel in designing and building beautiful open-plan living spaces that fit perfectly with your lifestyle and life stage.

What can Oliver James Garden Rooms do for your home? Create a wow-factor to welcome guests – in a stunning kitchen, eating and entertaining area. Bring the whole family together by seamlessly combining your living spaces. Combine your exterior and interior space using designer glazing and bi-folding doors. Maximise your reception-room space – providing infinite garden views and a designer look. Enhance the impact that strategically planned lighting schemes can create with the expertise of our outstanding lighting designers. Integrate remote controlled skylights that close automatically when they sense rain. Create a luxurious extension that will highlight your outdoor space whilst flooding your house with natural light.

Why do our designs work so well? We're recognised as leaders in our field, now shortlisted in the International Design and Architecture Awards 2012. We work with all our clients to unlock the perfect solutions to your living-space challenges. Thanks to the superior glass technology employed and the insulation properties used in construction, an Oliver James Garden Room is never too hot or too cold. Unlike conservatories, an Oliver James Garden Room does not need to be closed off from the house and works perfectly as part of your open-plan living space - all year round.

Contact us today Oliver James Garden Rooms: Experience a truly breath-taking, imaginative new way of living. We're proud to announce that our work has been shortlisted for the 2012 International Design and Architecture Awards.

Visit us and see what our clients say at: **www.OliverJamesGardenRooms.co.uk**
Call us on: **01908 367177** or e-mail us at: **info@OliverJamesGardenRooms.co.uk** to find out how we could transform your home – beautifully and functionally.

THE FOODIE GUIDE

Black *Dining Card*

or
£5 off
or
10% off

Expiry date: 30/9/2013

No:

see reverse for terms and conditions

Order your exclusive

Black *Dining Card*

LIMITED EDITION
only available to
THE FOODIE GUIDE
readers

Use your Black Dining Card as often as you like and *you* choose which offer you would prefer -
either a free Bottle of House Wine, £5 off **or** 10% off.

To apply for your Black Dining Card please fill in the form below and send (no stamp required) together with a cheque for £10 to:
FREEPOST RSKB-RHRA-RZBT, The Foodie Guide Ltd, 373 Welford Rd, Northampton, NN2 8PT.
Alternatively, order online at **www.thefoodieguide.co.uk**

Cardholder Name . . . .

Address . . . .

. . . .

. . . .

Postcode . . . .

Email . . . .

Tel. . . . .

To receive your exclusive Black Dining Card please enclose a cheque for £10
payable to The Square Design & Print Co Ltd. Only one card per cardholder will be
issued. Every card has a unique number and can only be issued once.
No replacements will be supplied. PLEASE READ THE RULES OF USE.

CARDHOLDER RULES OF USE

1. THE FOODIE GUIDE Black Dining Card may not be used in
   conjunction with any other offers, including FOODIE Vouchers.
2. The card entitles the cardholder to choose **either** £5 off, 10% off **or** a
   Bottle of House Wine when spending £30 or more on any day of the
   week and at any time, except on the following: **NOT ACCEPTED**
   during December, Mothers Day, Fathers Day or Valentines Day.
3. Only one card up to a maximum of 6 covers per table/party may be
   used with a minimum total spend of £30.
4. The card is only accepted at participating
   restaurants displaying The Black Dining Card
   symbol within THE FOODIE GUIDE Edition 10. **DC**
5. This card has no cash value and is valid until 30/09/2013.
6. Cardholders must mention THE FOODIE GUIDE Black Dining Card
   when making a telephone booking. Failure to do so may result in the
   offer being refused.

black dining card

Join the growing FOODIE family and visit our website

Become a "Taste Buddy" and recommend / review restaurants.
Visit the shop to order FOODIE vouchers, a black dining card or a book.
Watch video clips of local chefs at work or check out the latest news from
your favourite restaurants, delis and farm shops.

www.thefoodieguide.co.uk

THE FOODIE AWARD
2013

photograph courtesy of Murrays Restaurant, Whittlebury Hall

NOMINATE
YOUR FAVOURITE RESTAURANT
AND YOU COULD
WIN A MEAL FOR TWO!

We would like to hear from you, so nominate your favourite restaurant in Beds, Bucks, Herts or Northants for THE FOODIE Award. Just fill in the details below and send the form back to us. All forms returned to us by the closing date will be entered into a draw, the lucky winner of which will receive a meal for two at one of our four award winning restaurants.*

Please only nominate ONE establishment and take into consideration the quality of food, the service, the price and the surroundings before making your choice.

I would like to nominate: _____ **for THE FOODIE Award**

because _____

_____

Closing date for all nominations is 30th June 2013. (Winners of the current award will be published in the next edition of THE FOODIE GUIDE).

To be entered into the free draw please fill in your details below and then post back (NO STAMP REQUIRED) to:
Freepost RSKB-RHRA-RZBT, The Foodie Guide Ltd, 373 Welford Road, Northampton NN2 8PT.

Name: _____

Address: _____

_____ **Postcode:** _____

Telephone: _____ **Email:** _____

*Terms and conditions apply. The meal for two is excluding drinks.

We only include restaurants in THE FOODIE GUIDE which have been recommended by *you*, so please keep sending in your comments and together we shall maintain the high standard you expect.

You can send your comments via email to: paul@thefoodieguide.co.uk
or post to: Freepost RSKB-RHRA-RZBT, The Foodie Guide Ltd, 373 Welford Road, Northampton NN2 8PT.

Secret Diners are a select group of Foodies who eat out regularly and notice the good (and the not so good) and would like to tell us all about it. If you give us your name and address we will send you a restaurant assessment form which you can complete whenever you eat out, then just send your results back to us - it's easy!!

All Secret Diners receive 3 Foodie Vouchers per assessment and are entered into a draw to win a Foodie Hamper. Closing date for the draw is 30th June 2013.

WOULD YOU LIKE TO BE A SECRET DINER? **YES** ☐ **NO** ☐

ARE YOUR NAME AND ADDRESS DETAILS OVERLEAF? **YES** ☐ **NO** ☐ (if NO please enter your details below)

Name: _____

Address: _____

_____ Postcode: _____

Telephone: _____ Email: _____

extra vouchers ! FREE !

The Foodie Voucher
This voucher entitles the bearer on presentation to 10% discount off final bill inclusive of VAT

Valid only at participating establishments displaying a GOLD 10% symbol
Valid until 30th September 2013
See terms and conditions overleaf

10%

Now that you are a FOODIE GUIDE owner, we know you are serious about your food, so register your details with us and we will send you **2 extra FOODIE vouchers ABSOLUTELY FREE - or 4 vouchers if you fill in our survey on the reverse too**.

Please fill in your details below, tear this page out and send back (NO STAMP REQUIRED) to the following address:-
FREEPOST RSKB-RHRA-RZBT, The Foodie Guide Ltd, 373 Welford Road, Northampton NN2 8PT.

First Name: .... **Surname**: ....

Address:..

....

.... **Postcode**: ....

Email: ....

Tel: ....

If you would like to order extra copies of THE FOODIE GUIDE at **£6** each (**Postage & Packing FREE!!!!**) please send a cheque payable to The Square Design & Print Co Ltd and indicate how many copies you would like. Thank you.

Please send me [ ] copies. I enclose a cheque for [£]

THE FOODIE GUIDE Consumer Survey

1. Title: Mr / Mrs / Miss / Ms / Other (please state)

2. Name: . . . .

3. House No: . . . .

4. Postcode: . . . .

5. Email: . . . .

6. Age: Under 25 ☐   26-35 ☐   36-50 ☐   50+ ☐

7. What do you find most interesting/useful about The Foodie Guide (tick all that apply)

   Restaurants ☐   Chef Profiles ☐   Recipes ☐   Fine Foods & Wines ☐   Lifestyle ☐   Vouchers ☐

8. Do you use the vouchers?   Yes ☐   No ☐   (if no, go to question 11)

9. Which vouchers do you use most often?   £5 ☐   10% ☐   Bottle of wine ☐   Special ☐

10. How often do you use the vouchers

    weekly ☐   fortnightly ☐   monthly ☐   quarterly ☐   yearly ☐

11. If you don't use the vouchers is this because of the following (tick all that apply)

    Embarrassment ☐   Forgetting ☐   Not valuable enough ☐

    Restaurant doesn't accept vouchers ☐   Other (please state) ☐ . . . .

12. How often do you refer to The Foodie Guide

    weekly ☐   fortnightly ☐   monthly ☐   quarterly ☐   yearly ☐

13. Would you buy The Foodie Guide as a gift for somebody?   Yes ☐   No ☐

14. What's the best feature of The Foodie Guide?

15. What's the worst feature of The Foodie Guide? . . . .

16. How would you improve The Foodie Guide? . . . .

17. Which vouchers would you like for filling in this survey?

    £5 ☐   10% ☐   Bottle of wine ☐

18. Any other feedback . . . .

    . . . .